THE BASIC FACTS OF HUMAN HEREDITY

THE BASIC FACTS OF

HUMAN HEREDITY

AMRAM SCHEINFELD

19.10.63

PAN BOOKS LTD : LONDON

First published 1961 in the U.S.A.
by the Washington Square Press Inc.
First edition published in the U.K. 1963 by
PAN BOOKS LTD
8 Headfort Place, London, S.W.1

This is a revised and expanded edition of
The Human Heredity Handbook, published
by the J. B. Lippincott Company, U.S.A.

*Printed in Great Britain by Richard Clay and Company, Ltd.,
Bungay, Suffolk*

PREFACE

THE SUBJECT OF human heredity, which long has fascinated people – no doubt from the time they began to think about themselves – has never been more important than it is today.

For one thing, the science of human genetics, which deals with this subject, has developed enormously within recent years, and a vast amount of new information about every aspect of human inheritance has become available. For another thing, world-wide concern has arisen about the possibility that atomic explosions may cause serious damage to human hereditary factors. Thus, terms such as 'chromosomes' and 'genes' (the hereditary units), and 'mutations' (changes in these units), which were unknown to most persons a few decades ago, now have become household words.

As human beings have advanced there also has come an increased feeling of responsibility with respect to the bearing and rearing of children, and the desire to ensure for those brought into the world every opportunity to be as healthy in body and mind as possible. Moreover, with the destinies of all branches of mankind becoming ever more closely interwoven, the interest in human inheritance must now spread far beyond individuals and their families to people everywhere.

All of this has made it essential for every thinking and conscientious person to have an adequate knowledge of how the process of heredity works, and how it interacts with the forces of environment to make each of us what he or she is and what our children are or will be. It is with the thought of providing authoritative information on these points, and of presenting the material clearly, interestingly, and concisely – and at a price low enough to be within the reach of everyone – that this book, *The Basic Facts of Human Heredity*, has been prepared and published.

(While fashioned in large part from an earlier work of the author's, *The Human Heredity Handbook*, this new book has been extensively revised and up-dated to include much recent material, and also has been greatly changed in format. At the same time, like its predecessor, this book has derived much of its data, and some of its illustrations, from the author's major work on the subject, *You and Heredity* and its successive editions.)

Although conciseness has been indeed a principal objective in preparing this book, there has been no departure from the aim of achieving the utmost in accuracy as well. To that end much valuable aid, which I gratefully acknowledge, was given by a number of my esteemed professional friends who read sections of the manuscript, among them Drs C. Nash Herndon and Herbert L. Cooper, Professor David Wechsler and the late Professor Irving Lorge. To conform to the copyright laws, I also hereby formally thank myself and my American publishers, J. B. Lippincott Company, for permission to use or adapt a number of illustrations from *The New* YOU AND HEREDITY. Further, I wish to thank the editors of this edition for making a number of special changes or additions, to be noted in the text where they appear, which should add to the book's usefulness for British readers.

Finally, I might say that many important facts in this book have come through the research activities of British geneticists and other scientists, with a gratifying number of whom I have had the pleasure and privilege of enjoying a personal acquaintanceship over the years.

AMRAM SCHEINFELD

CONTENTS

LIST OF ILLUSTRATIONS

To my beloved wife

Dorothy

Human Chromosomes

As they look (after staining) under the microscope. Magnification about 1,500 times

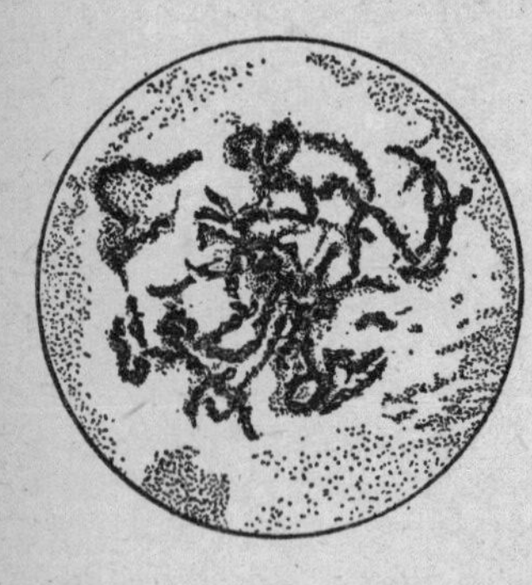

1. The 46 chromosomes in the stretched-out stage. (Some of the chromosomes in this picture, and the one below, are hidden by others, so the full 46 cannot be counted.)

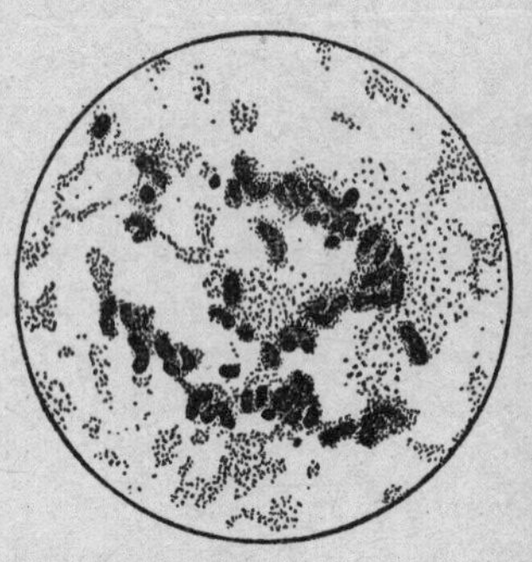

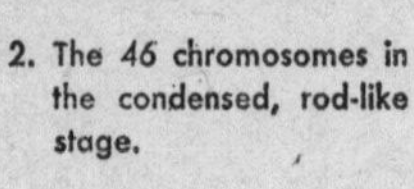

2. The 46 chromosomes in the condensed, rod-like stage.

3. Diagram of a greatly magnified chromosome section, showing the beads or segments that contain the genes.

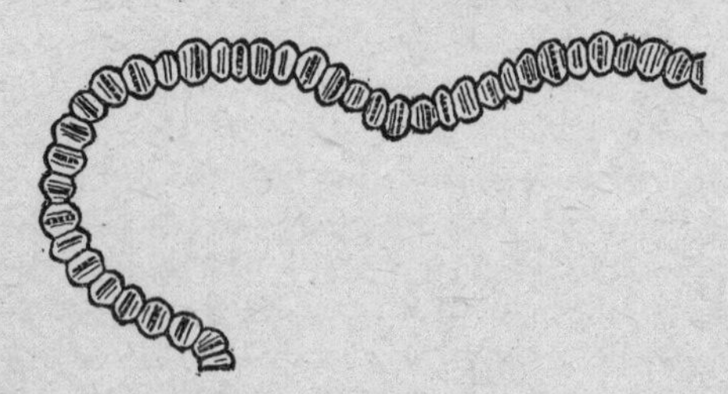

CHAPTER ONE

HEREDITY AND ENVIRONMENT

WE HEAR PEOPLE say, 'I don't believe in heredity – I believe in environment.' Or, 'I think environment is more important than heredity.' Others say, 'That whole family is just no good – drunks, criminals, paupers – it's because they've got rotten heredity.' Or, 'Some groups are born to be superior, other groups to be inferior, and the quickest way to improve humanity is to breed out the inferior people.' All such statements are based on wrong ideas as to what heredity means, how it works, and what part it does or does not play in people's lives. These misconceptions have caused much suffering, injustice, confusion, and unhappiness from the beginning of mankind's history. But at last, after decades of intensive study, the science of *genetics* which deals with heredity has cleared the air to a vast extent and has provided many positive, accurate answers in place of previous myths and fallacies. This book, then, will try to present the facts about human heredity as scientists now know them, and to indicate how you, the reader, can usefully apply these facts to increase your understanding of yourself, your children, and your fellow men.

What is 'heredity'? First, it is what makes us what we are as members of a particular species – in our case, human beings. When a woman is pregnant, we know definitely that she is not going to give birth to a little elephant, kangaroo, mouse, or bird, but to a *human* baby. We know that this child will have a *human* nose, not a snout or beak; *human* hands and feet, not hoofs or claws; a *human* brain, heart, lungs, skin, etc. In countless details, then, it is heredity that causes human beings to produce offspring who are like themselves and like no other living things, just as it is heredity that causes all other creatures – dogs, cats, chickens, fish, apes, etc. – to produce offspring of their own kind. Further, heredity has much to do with producing the resemblances between individual parents and their offspring, and among members of the same family groups, in numerous physical and mental traits.

What about 'environment'? That, too, is extremely important in making people what they are. By 'environment' we mean everything *outside* the individual and his inherited factors, from conception on. Before birth the environment is the mother's womb, the nourishment she supplies to the embryo baby, and all the conditions under which he or she develops. After the baby is born, the environment includes not only what he is fed and how he is cared for, but everything he sees, hears, and is able to learn. As the child grows, his upbringing, surroundings, emotional life, hygienic conditions, medical care, experiences, playmates, schooling, attitudes of others – all these are increasingly important parts of his environment. No matter how good a child's heredity, a very bad environment may ruin his chances of becoming a healthy, useful, well-adjusted person. Equally, no matter how good the environment, a child with very bad or defective heredity may not be able to survive, or to develop normally and successfully.

From what has been said, it should be clear that heredity and environment are not opposing forces, working always against one another. Rather, they are complementary forces, always working together. Every human being and every other living thing are products of both heredity and environment. Without both there could be no life, nor any particular type of creature. Everything you are, and everything anyone can be made to be, depends always on the *potentialities* of heredity, working together with the *possibilities* of environment. Very good heredity can often offset some of the disadvantages of poor environment, as has been proved in the cases of Abraham Lincoln, George Washington Carver and many other great people who worked their way to the top against heavy odds. And very good environment can often help to make up for some of the lacks of heredity. For instance, kindly and expert training can cause a child born with inherited blindness, or some crippling condition, to become a happy and well-adjusted person. Fortunately, *most* human beings are born with pretty good heredity, and more and more persons today are growing up in good environments.

One may still hear arguments over which is more important – heredity or environment. But this once-popular subject for school debates or informal arguments now arouses only an indulgent smile from the scientist, who knows that the question as posed has no meaning. One can only ask it with respect to *particular* aspects or traits of inheritance. As stated before, both heredity and environment are essential to produce and sustain any living thing. So, in general terms, neither force can be called 'more important' than the other. However, in a garden the very same environment produces many species of flowers and vegetables, depending on which *seeds* were planted. Thus, in producing any particular kind of flower or vegetable, heredity can be called far more important than environment. Likewise, from the same prenatal environment in a mother may come two non-identical twins – one a girl, one a boy; one blue-eyed, one black-eyed, one normal-sighted, one colour-blind. In producing these differences between the children (including their sex), heredity is again vastly more important than environment. But if a baby is born with a serious defect purely because of a pre-natal accident, or some dietary deficiency, obviously in that case environment is the all-important factor. As we proceed with this book, and take up particular traits of numerous kinds, we will see at work every degree of both hereditary and environmental influence.

CHAPTER TWO

THE NEW BABY

THE CONCEPTION OF a new baby takes place the instant a sperm from the father enters and fertilizes an egg waiting in the mother. Usually one egg every four weeks is produced by a woman (although sometimes two or more are produced, which may give rise to twins, triplets, etc.). The egg comes out of either of the two ovaries and moves down into one of the two Fallopian tubes. Here the egg is ready to be fertilized.

In the act of intercourse the male propels into the female's vagina many millions of sperms (from 50,000,000 to 500,000,000 in an average single ejaculation). These sperms are so small millions could be packed into a pinhead. Like the tiniest imaginable tadpoles, they swim first in the stream of seminal fluid, then in the secretions of the vagina and womb. Only a small proportion get into the womb, and fewer still into the tubes. But should any sperms reach the egg, the moment a single one enters there is an instantaneous toughening of the covering of the egg which shuts out all other sperms. Thus, of all the millions of sperms entering the race, only a single one can win out and fertilize the egg.

If we could look through a powerful microscope and follow the process of conception we would see this: As the sperm enters the egg, leaving its tail outside, the sperm-head opens and out comes a batch of twenty-three tiny little wormlike bits of living substance. At the same time a little globule inside the egg (the *nucleus*) also opens up, and out comes another batch of twenty-three of the same tiny little wormlike things. These little things in both the sperm and the egg are called *chromosomes*. They carry *everything a child inherits* from the parents. (See illustration, frontispiece.)

As we examine the chromosomes more closely, we find that among those in each set – whether the twenty-three from the father or the twenty-three from the mother – one may differ from another in shape and size. But there is a more remarkable fact. Every chromosome from the father finds an exactly matching type of its same shape and size, among the chromosomes waiting in the mother's egg. (An exception, in the sex chromosomes, will be explained in Chapter 4.) How the chromosomes look if those from the two parents are arranged in pairs is shown in our accompanying illustration.

Individual Human Chromosomes

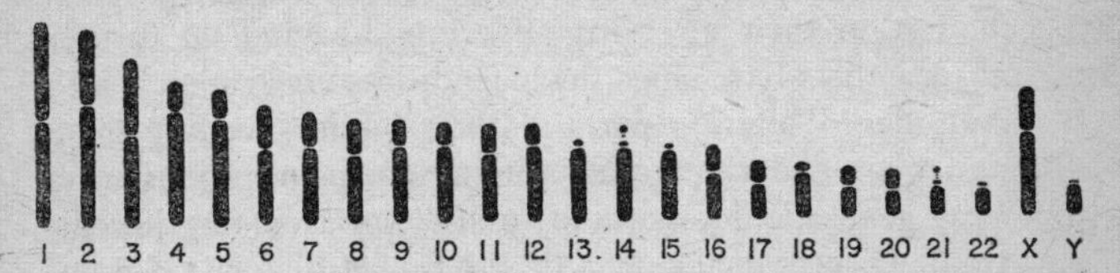

This chart (idiogram) shows the different types of chromosomes of a male, arranged in order of relative size and/or form. The chromosomes identified by numbers, from 1 to 22, are the 'autosomes', a pair of each number (or 44 'autosomes' in all), being found in every normal cell. The X and Y (the additional two, making 46), are the male's sex chromosomes. In a female the numbered chromosomes are the same, but the sex chromosomes consist of two X's. (Idiogram by Drs Ernest H. Y. Chu and Norman H. Giles, *Amer. Jour. Human Genetics*, March, 1959. Reproduced by permission.)

Most often, when chromosomes are seen under a microscope, they are in a compressed form (which gives them their wormlike appearance). But at certain stages they stretch out, and then we find that each chromosome actually consists of hundreds of clear, jelly-like sections, strung together like beads. These sections contain the *genes* (pronounced 'jeans'). And it is these genes that act like wonderful little chemical workers to carry out the processes of heredity. Every gene differs from the others in some way, and has some special job to do in the fashioning and developing of a baby, from conception to birth. But even after birth, and throughout life, the genes continue their work.

One of the most important aspects of the genes and the process of heredity is this. The genes as they pass along from generation to generation *are not changed in their workings* by any changes parents make in their own traits or that are made in their traits by environment. Establishment of this fact has upset the old theory of the *inheritance of acquired characteristics* – that traits acquired by persons during their lifetimes, or environmental changes made in them, could indeed be transmitted to their offspring. The theory has been disproved by many experiments. Even before the science of genetics came into being, scientists had taken note of the fact that generations of binding of feet among Chinese, circumcision among Jews, mutilations among primitive peoples (enlarging lips, scarring faces, tattooing, etc.), had in no way produced any corresponding changes in their newborn offspring. Leaving no further doubts, scientists have since made countless experiments with lower animals – altering parts of their bodies, feeding them different diets and chemicals, training them in various ways for many generations – without in any way changing hereditary traits. (Sensational claims by the Soviet biologist, Lysenko, that he had 'proved' the acquired-characteristics theory correct appear now to be discredited even in his own country.) How and why the genes retain their identity can now be best understood by looking into the processes through which eggs and sperms are formed.

When a little girl baby is born, she already has in her tiny ovaries all the eggs – in rudimentary form – that will take mature shape and emerge after she achieves puberty. And within each rudimentary egg there already are present exact replicas of all the chromosomes and genes that the girl baby received from her parents at conception, and from which will be drawn all the chromosomes her own children will receive. An immediate question, then, is this: In what possible way could the genes so tightly enclosed in the eggs (whether rudimentary or mature) suddenly be made to change in conformity with anything or everything happening to the female in whose ovaries they are? It is obviously ridiculous to think that if a dark-haired girl bleached her hair blonde, that would make her dark-hair genes suddenly turn into blonde genes. Or if she got her straight hair permanently waved, that would cause her straight-hair genes to change suddenly so that her baby would be born with wavy hair. But it is no less ridiculous to assume that whenever a mother, or future mother, makes a change in any other trait of her body, mind, or character (or any such change is made in her), the results will immediately cause the genes concerned with that trait to change their workings in conformity with the new requirements.

Human Sperms and Egg

HUMAN SPERMS

Magnified as here shown about 400 times. (Actual size of sperm is about 1/400 of an inch long.)

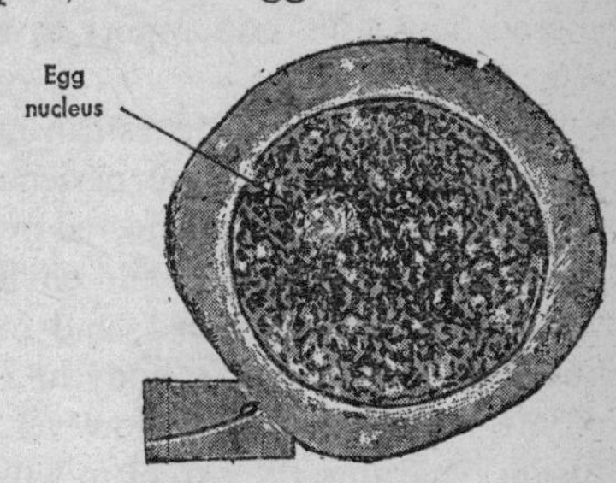

HUMAN EGG

Relative size shown by sperm entering it. The egg nucleus contains the chromosomes. The rest is food material.

(Adapted from actual photographs in the author's book, *The New YOU AND HEREDITY*. Copyright 1939, 1950 by Amram Scheinfeld.)

As with a girl baby, a boy baby, too, when he is born, already has set aside within him all the 'germ cells' from which will some day come his contributions to his children's heredity. A difference between the sexes is that while in the female the eggs themselves are already present at birth, in the male the sperms do not begin to be fashioned by the germ cells until he achieves puberty. Another difference is that while the eggs of the female are limited in number (because she will usually produce no more than one a month for a period of about thirty years), the sperm production of the male, once it begins, goes on into the billions and billions, often throughout his lifetime. But except for the difference in numbers, the sperms of a male are the same as the eggs of a female with respect to the nature of their genes. In the male, too, all the genes carried in his sperms are exact replicas of those which he received from his parents at conception, and cannot be changed in their workings by any changes that are made in his own traits. (*Note*: How some changes, or 'mutations', do occur in genes in rare instances will be explained in later chapters. These gene changes are different from those we have discussed, and give no support to the 'acquired-characteristic' theory.)

Although a child's genes can in no way be changed by the parents' acts, habits, or experiences, this hardly means that a child's *traits* will not be affected by these influences. Obviously, parents can affect their child environmentally in a great many ways, from birth onward; and in the mother's case, her influences on the child's body and mind may begin from the moment of conception. However, there has been much confusion regarding the extent to which the mother's condition is responsible for various traits appearing in babies. Often conditions which are blamed on prenatal factors are due to heredity, and at other times the reverse is true.

The developing baby is in no sense ever a part of the mother's body. Though growing within her, the baby is always a distinct individual (as courts have ruled). Biologically there is a wall – the *placenta* – between the mother and baby. The mother's blood, which carries the nourishment, stops on one side of the wall and the blood elements are broken down and strained through it. There is therefore no more *direct blood tie* between a mother and child than between a father and child. The baby manufactures its own blood according to the formula prescribed by its blood genes. In fact, the baby's blood may be so different chemically from the mother's – for instance, with respect to the Rh factor – that an interchange of blood substances may sometimes cause serious damage.

Other hazards to the unborn baby may be these: *germs*, if the mother has any germ disease; *alcohol*, if the mother is a heavy drinker; *drugs*, if the mother is an addict, abnormal *hormonal or chemical states* in the mother; or *dietary deficiencies.* Any of these factors – which, fortunately, occur in only a minority of the cases – may disturb the normal development of a baby, and produce various congenital diseases, defects, or abnormalities which may be mistakenly regarded as hereditary. (*See note at end of Chapter.*)

The basis of many popular myths about *prenatal impressions* has been the belief that what goes on in the mother's mind can have profound effects on the baby she is carrying: that marks or deformities could develop in a baby in resemblance to something which strongly impressed or frightened the mother during pregnancy; that by her listening to good music her child would be more musical; or by her reading elevating books the child would be brainier, etc. Actually there is no nerve connexion between the mother and the baby, and no way her thoughts could reach the child – and certainly no way that her thinking could affect the child's genes. All that might happen is that her mental and nervous state, if good, might benefit her physical state, and therefore help the child, or, contrariwise, if she is badly upset during pregnancy, the nourishment and environment for the child might be worsened.

While the genes the mother transmits to her baby are exactly the same whatever her age (since her eggs with their quotas of genes were formed before her own birth), the prenatal environment she provides may change as she grows older. For one thing, ageing is apt to bring more diseases, internal upsets, and disorders. Thus, with older mothers (mostly those beyond the late thirties), the risk of defects and abnormalities in babies may increase. However, if the mother is healthy and fit in all ways, her age by itself may affect the child very little.

As for the father, once he has made his contribution to the child's heredity at conception, by way of the sperm, his influence on the child's traits can be only those exerted after it is born. But as in the mother's case, the 'like father, like son' theory often confuses environmental influences with hereditary effects. If a father's (or mother's) alcoholism, criminality, degeneracy, or other bad traits are repeated in children, this need not at all mean that heredity is responsible. Nor can the repetition of good traits of behaviour and temperament be necessarily credited to heredity. In every case the home environment and the hereditary histories of *both* parents must be weighed together.

Unlike the situation with the mother, the age of the father has nothing to do with the prenatal condition or development of a child. This follows from the fact that the *genes* in the father's sperms are in no way changed by his ageing. So long as a man can go on producing fertile sperms (and some men have done so into their nineties), these sperms will be exactly the same in the quality and workings of their genes, and the traits they can produce in children, as the sperms of the man when he was young and robust. (The statement may be no surprise to livestock experts, who know that thoroughbred stallions and blooded bulls can be mated into their relatively old ages, without any deterioration in the quality of the offspring.) Nor will the fact that a man has been seriously disabled in a war or an accident, or has acquired a serious disease, affect the *heredity* of his children.

The 'Thalidomide babies' of recent years offered the most tragic examples of how certain drugs taken by pregnant mothers could maim their babies unalterably. Before the effects of thalidomide – a supposedly 'safe' sleeping pill and sedative – became known and its use by pregnant women halted, more than 2,000 infants with badly deformed or totally absent limbs were born because of it, many in England and Canada, but most in Germany where the drug had been introduced. Of special interest is the fact that similar abnormalities, such as 'congenital amputations', have in rare instances been produced by hereditary defects.

CHAPTER THREE

THE WORKINGS OF HEREDITY

THE BASIC PRINCIPLES of heredity were discovered by an Austrian monk, Gregor Mendel, in 1857. He was the abbot of a monastery at Brno (then in Austria, now in Czechoslovakia) where he had a garden in which he experimented. One series of Mendel's experiments, crossbreeding sweet peas of different varieties, brought to light the facts about inheritance which are now called the 'Mendelian laws.' These 'laws', or principles, follow:

1. Inherited traits are produced by separate factors (the genes) which pass along unchanged from one generation to another.

2. The genes come in pairs in individuals, one of every pair from each parent, and if two paired genes differ in their effects, one usually dominates the other, and may be called 'dominant', whereas the weaker gene, whose effects are suppressed, may be called 'recessive'.

3. When seeds are formed in plants (or sperms or eggs are formed in any animal or human), the two genes of each pair in the parent separate or segregate, and only one of each pair goes to an offspring. Which gene of a given pair goes into any seed, sperm, or egg is independent of which gene of another pair goes into the same seed, sperm, or egg. That is to say, if a plant has dominant genes producing red colouring and tallness, but also carries hidden recessive genes for white colour and shortness, the red and tall genes might or might not go into the same seed. One seed could as easily get the red and short genes together, and another the white and tall genes.

The importance of Mendel's discoveries was not realized until after 1900, when various investigators checked and found that the Mendelian laws apparently applied to inheritance in all living things, including human beings. However, in time it was shown that these laws needed certain qualifications and modifications. The most important strides in clarifying and extending the knowledge of heredity came through the researches of the late, great Professor Thomas Hunt Morgan and his brilliant Columbia University team, which included the now-famous Professor H. J. Muller (who, like Professor Morgan, was awarded a Nobel Prize). These scientists and others, experimenting mainly with fruit flies (*Drosophila*), worked out many of the detailed principles and techniques that form the foundation of the science of modern genetics.

Today we know that each gene is a living molecule – a tiny bit of the living substance *protoplasm.* (More precisely, the gene is a protein molecule with its most vital constituent being 'DNA' – *deoxyribonucleic acid.*) As chemists know, there are countless types and varieties of molecules, each with different properties, depending on the number, kind, and arrangement of the atoms of which they are composed. So, too, there are countless types and varieties of gene-molecules, or genes. First, the genes of one species are different from those of other species. Cat genes are different from dog genes, cow genes from horse genes, ape genes from monkey genes. And human genes, of course, are different from the genes of all other animals – which is mainly why we are so different from them. Further, among human beings themselves, as within each species of other animals, there are different gradations and varieties of the genes for given traits. This in turn helps to explain (but is not the only reason) why one individual may be so different from another in a great many ways.

We also know that each gene has a special chemical effect, or series of effects, on the materials that come into the individual, from conception onwards. In some respects a gene acts like an *enzyme* or *catalyst*, a substance that converts other substances into changed forms – as yeast causes dough to rise, or rennet turns milk into junket. When a baby is conceived, all of his genes begin to work on the raw materials in the fertilized egg, later on the food materials coming in from the mother.

Varieties of Genes

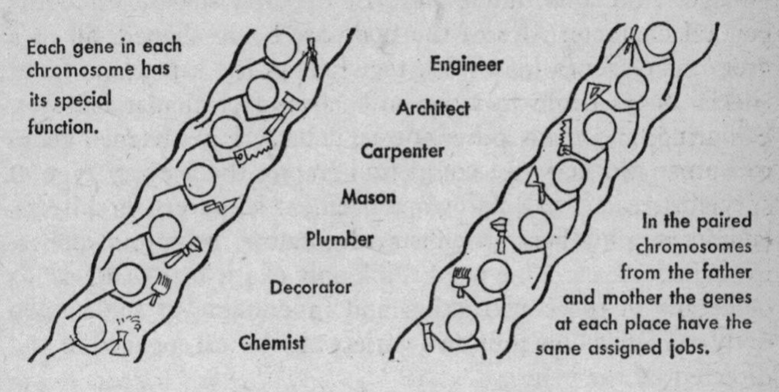

- But genes may do their jobs in different ways:

BULLY genes (dominant) may keep weaker ones (recessive) from working.

FREAK genes work peculiarly to produce various oddities in the body.

TEMPERAMENTAL genes (qualified) work unexpectedly and only under some circumstances.

RIP VAN WINKLE genes (late onset) may sleep for years and then awake to action.

BUSY-BODY genes (multi-action) do various jobs at once, and sometimes wreck many jobs.

VILLAIN genes produce serious defects and diseases, and sometimes cause early death.

Through continuous stages the genes help to form many types of cells, produce flesh, bones, and muscles, construct organs and get functions under way. In the first stages, when the general characteristics of the body are being shaped, all or a great many genes may work together on the same job. Later special genes begin to work on shapes of particular features, colouring, and many other special details. If we likened genes to human workers, we could find among them every type of specialist, each with its own capacities: labourers, architects, engineers, plumbers, chemists, decorators, sculptors, dieticians, doctors, etc. One need think only of the many thousands of details in the construction and functioning of the human body to realize how infinite a variety of jobs are engaged in and directed by the genes.

One of the most important properties of the genes is their capacity for reproducing themselves. (It is mainly in this way that genes, as living molecules, differ from any mineral or non-living molecules.) The self-reproduction of the genes begins and proceeds with fantastic rapidity from the moment a new baby is conceived. As we saw in Chapter 2, the father's sperm brings into the egg twenty-three separate chromosomes – each a string of genes. Waiting in the mother's egg are another twenty-three chromosomes. Immediately, the chromosomes and their genes begin to 'fatten up' on the material in the egg, and each gene doubles in size (or builds a replica alongside itself). Then, as each fattened chromosome splits in two lengthwise, each doubled gene at the same time also divides. Finally the cell housing the chromosomes pinches together, and the two halves separate, so that there now are two cells, each with exact duplicates of all the original forty-six chromosomes and their genes. (See illustration.) The process is repeated again and again, the two cells becoming four, the four eight, the eight sixteen, etc., into the millions, billions, and trillions. (It is estimated that a baby at birth has about twenty-six trillion cells, with the same genes in each cell. The total number of these genes is still unknown. Present estimates range very roughly from a minimum of about 40,000 to 60,000 or more genes in the twenty-three pairs of human chromosomes.)

While the chromosomes and genes that go into every cell are exactly the same, the cells as they form and develop are *not* the same. This is because with each step in the cell-multiplication process, somewhat as with material in a house being built, cells at different points are shaped and constructed in different ways. Under the direction of the specialist genes we mentioned previously, cell clusters take different forms. Some turn into the outer parts of the body – skin, muscles, features;

How Chromosomes Multiply

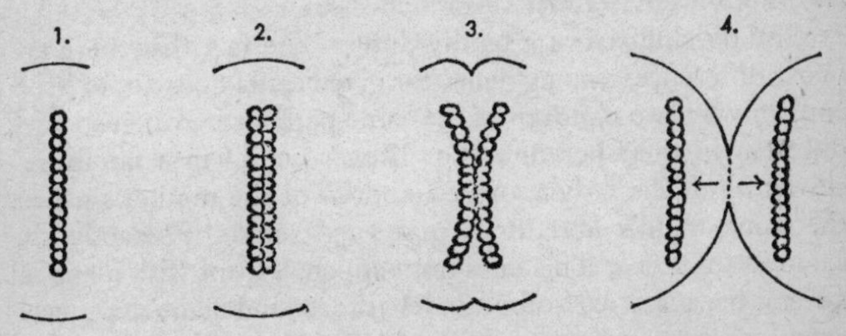

(1) Section of one of the original 46 chromosomes in a fertilized egg cell.

(2) Each gene in the chromosome creates a replica of itself.

(3) When the genes are duplicated, the doubled chromosome splits. This has been occurring likewise in all the other 45 chromosomes in the egg cell.

(4) The duplicated chromosomes move apart and the cell divides, forming two cells, each housing exact duplicates of all the original 46 chromosomes.

some into the skeletal framework; some into the internal mechanisms – brain and nervous system, heart and arteries, digestive system, glands, etc. Precisely how this is done (or how experts believe it is done) is far too complicated to explain here. But there is no guess about *what* is done. Innumerable studies of embryos show up to what point the body construction has been carried out at every successive stage. And the fact that at any given stage – four weeks, eight weeks, twelve weeks, etc. – the development of any normal baby is almost identical with that of any other is proof of how remarkably systematic and precise the human genes are in their workings.

Apart from completing given stages of the baby's development at prescribed times, the 'specialist' genes are highly individual in their work, just as are human architects, carpenters, decorators, engineers, etc. One eye-colour gene may make eyes dark, another may be set on making them light blue, another green, etc. For hair colour there are black, brown, blond, and red genes. Innumerable other differences in genes account largely for the varieties of human features and body details, and to a greater or lesser extent for differences in physical and mental functioning, and in fitness or defectiveness (always allowing for environmental influences).

Why do children of a family differ? The fact that there are many differences among genes for given traits does not of itself explain why two children of the same parents are often so very different in their heredity. For if every child in a family received *all* of the father's genes, and *all* of the mother's genes, then one child's hereditary make-up would be exactly the same as another's. This does not happen (except with identical twins) because, as noted under the Mendelian laws, each sperm of the father carries only *half* of his chromosomes, and each egg of the mother carries only *half* of hers. In other words, when a man produces sperms there is a process whereby for every two sperms, his twenty-three pairs of chromosomes sort out into two groups, with *only one chromosome of each pair* going in each group, around which a sperm then takes shape. Thus, every sperm contains twenty-three *single* chromosomes. When eggs are formed in the female there is a similar process whereby each egg gets only one of each pair of her chromosomes, so that it also carries only twenty-three single chromosomes.

In either parent's case, which chromosomes of any pair go into which sperms is entirely a matter of chance. The process is much like a shuffling and dealing out of cards, but with chromosomes being dealt out instead. One sperm might get a combination of chromosomes quite different or even entirely

How Heredity Works

Father's chromosomes

Each parent has 23 pairs of chromosomes, or 46 in all.

Mother's chromosomes

When father produces sperms, each sperm gets only half of his chromosomes.

When mother produces eggs, each egg gets only half of her chromosomes.

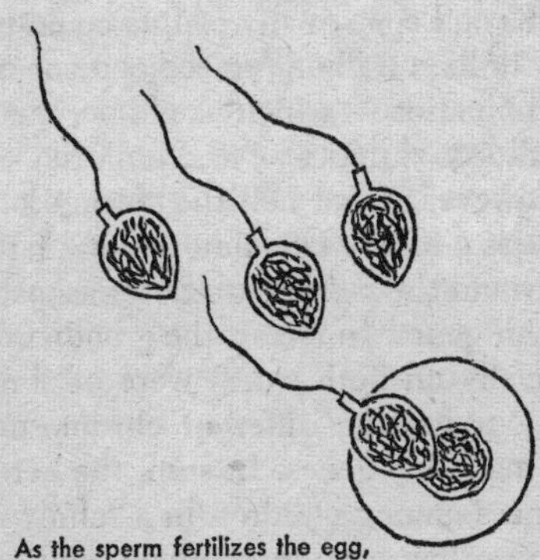

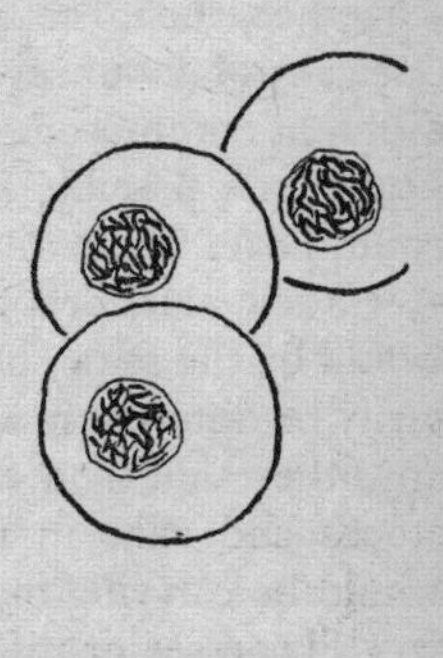

As the sperm fertilizes the egg, the 23 chromosomes from the father join with the 23 chromosomes from the mother.

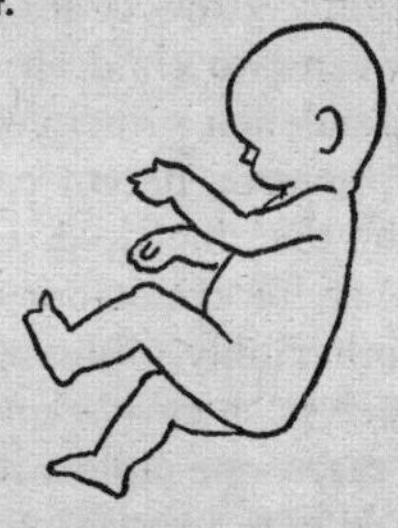

The combined 46 chromosomes work to produce all of the baby's hereditary traits.

different from those in another sperm; or again, most of the chromosomes in two sperms might be the same. This is equally true for the chromosomes in the mother's eggs. But the chances that any two children in a family (other than identical twins) would get exactly the same chromosome combinations – or completely different chromosomes – is extremely remote, for reasons which follow.

Taking at random one out of each of the twenty-three pairs of chromosomes carried by every man – this chromosome out of one pair, that chromosome out of another pair – it would be possible for him to produce sperms with 8,388,608 different chromosome combinations. A woman's eggs, likewise, could carry any of 8,388,608 different chromosome combinations. Together, then, the sperms and eggs of any couple could produce any of about seventy million million (70,000,000,000,000) different chromosome combinations – which would be, theoretically, the possible hereditary varieties of the children they could have. Ordinarily, however, about half the chromosomes – or a few more or a few less – of any two children of a family would be the same. Nor would the *unlike* chromosomes necessarily be different in all their genes. In fact, if the grandparents on either side (and especially on both sides) were of similar stocks and alike in many traits, the different chromosomes would be carrying many matching genes. In sum, the hereditary likenesses or differences among children in a family will depend on how many genes they have in common, and what differences there are in their other genes.

How a difference in only a few genes can often produce a marked difference between two children of a family becomes clear if we recall the Mendelian principle regarding dominant and recessive genes. Suppose a parent carries a gene of each type for a given trait, and that one child receives the dominant, the other the recessive; as for eye colour, if one child receives a black-eye gene, the other only a blue-eye gene; or for hair form, if one child receives a curly gene, the other only a straight gene. In these cases, one child will show the dominant trait, and if another child gets a recessive gene from each parent, he will show the recessive trait. The differences with respect to most traits may be unimportant. But there are some genetic situations where a single dominant gene (or its absence) in one child, and not in another, can produce striking differences in their appearance, mentality, talent, health, or strength and in the whole course of their lives. Examples of these genetic situations, and of various others, will be found in succeeding chapters.

We have previously stated that the genes a parent passes on to a child are unaltered by any changes the parent has made (or that have been made) in his own traits during his or her lifetime. But we also noted that in extremely rare instances a gene *can be changed* in its workings (though not in accordance with any change in the parent's traits). The gene change or *mutation* to which we refer may take place if a gene in one of the germ cells of a prospective father or a mother is 'hit' or disturbed by some outside force in such a way as to shake up, rearrange, or alter the atoms composing it. Under natural conditions, cosmic rays, chemicals, and perhaps other outside influences can produce mutations, as they have been doing from the beginning of life on earth. These natural gene changes, accumulating through the ages, have been responsible for producing the infinite varieties of genes among human beings and all other livings things; and in our own time spontaneous mutations, as they have been capitalized on, have made possible the breeding of many new types of domestic animals, plants, and flowers.

However, it should be stressed that in the great majority of cases mutations are very slight; that in only about one in one hundred instances are they beneficial or useful; and that for the rest, they tend mostly to produce defects in the genes which, under natural conditions, would eventually cause such genes to be weeded out. The possibilities that have begun to loom up with respect to the mutation-inducing effects of radiation – particularly through atomic and hydrogen bombs – will be discussed in Chapter 27.

Altogether, as the reader will find, the facts about human heredity uncovered by scientists are mostly on the optimistic side. Many conditions formerly regarded as due to bad or defective inheritance have been traced to bad environments; and as environments have improved, the incidence of these conditions and their threats have been greatly reduced. Even where conditions are known to be hereditary, recent findings have in many instances helped to lessen the fears regarding them. Not least among the helpful developments has been the disproof of old theories about the inheritance of acquired characteristics. Parents now know that any mistakes they made, any diseases, defects, or bad habits they acquired, or any shortcomings developed by unfavourable environments, did not 'soak into' their genes, and cannot be transmitted to their children. At the same time, what parents have learned to advantage can be transmitted to their children through improved environment and proper training. The forces of heredity still remain and always will be vastly powerful. But more can be done now to give good heredity – with which the great majority of people are endowed – a chance to assert itself, and to keep bad heredity – which is found in only a very small proportion of people – from doing its worst.

CHAPTER FOUR

THE BABY'S SEX

'WE WANT A BOY,' or 'We want a girl,' a couple may say. Isn't there something parents can do beforehand to make their wish as to the baby's sex come true? Not yet! Throughout the ages parents have had the same thought, and countless sex-determining formulas and treatment have been employed. All those in the past were worthless because they were based on false notions and superstitions about the way in which a baby's sex is determined. But even today, although we *do* know what causes a baby to be a boy or a girl – as we shall presently see – there is still no way of insuring the desired results. The sex of the baby continues to be a matter of chance – although it need not always remain so.

The sex of every baby is fixed at the moment of conception. The deciding factor comes not through the mother, but through the *father's contribution.* Whether the baby will be a boy or a girl depends simply on which *of two types of sperms from the father enters the egg first.* One kind of sperm leads to the production of a boy. The other kind of sperm results in a girl. The mother's egg is neutral. When it is fertilized it can work to produce either a boy or a girl, depending on which kind of sperm enters the egg and starts the development of the baby.

Hereditary factors – chromosomes and their genes – determine the baby's sex, as they do other inherited traits. In Chapter 2 we saw that at conception every child receives forty-six chromosomes – a set of twenty-three from the father, a set of twenty-three from the mother. In each of these two sets, one special chromosome is called the sex chromosome because it is concerned with the determination of the baby's sex. These sex chromosomes are of two types. One type is very long, containing many genes, and is called the 'X' chromosome. The other is very short, with few genes, and is called the 'Y' chromosome. And the whole difference to start with between what will be a girl, and what will be a boy, is that the girl gets *two* X chromosomes, or an XX combination; the boy gets only *one* X, *plus one* Y – an XY combination.

How are the sex chromosomes transmitted? When a woman produces eggs, there is a process whereby each egg receives replicas of only *half* of her chromosomes – or *one* chromosome of each of her twenty-three pairs. Since her sex chromosomes are *both* X's, one X will go into every egg. Thus, the mother transmits an X chromosome to *every* child. But the father's contribution works differently. When he produces sperms, there also is a process whereby each sperm receives only *one* of every pair of his chromosomes. So, since his sex chromosomes are of two kinds, X and Y, his sperms will also be of two kinds. Of every two sperms the man produces, an X chromosome will go into one, a Y into the other. Which means that of the tens of millions of sperms which a father releases at a given time, exactly half are X-bearers, half Y-bearers.

As the millions of sperms enter the womb and move up in the tube where the egg is waiting, one may think of sex determination as a race between the Y's and the X's to get to the egg first and win it for the male side or the female side. Since the egg already carries one X, as we have seen, the baby's sex will depend on whether the entering sperm carries another X, or carries a Y. (Only a single sperm decides because, the moment one sperm enters, all the others are shut out.) Thus, if an X sperm wins out, it will join with the X already there and an XX individual – a girl baby – will be started on her way. But if a Y wins, the result will be an XY individual – a boy. All this is shown in our accompanying diagram. Study it and fix it in your mind. The facts will come up many times in this book, and in your life.

How does the XX combination cause the baby to develop as a girl, the XY combination to develop as a boy? The answer lies in the fact that while sex genes are found in various chromosomes, the X is heavily loaded with femaleness genes, whereas the other chromosomes together carry more maleness genes. In addition, the Y may have some especially potent maleness genes. So, if an X-bearing sperm enters the egg, joining with the X already there, the combined femaleness genes

How a Baby's Sex Is Determined

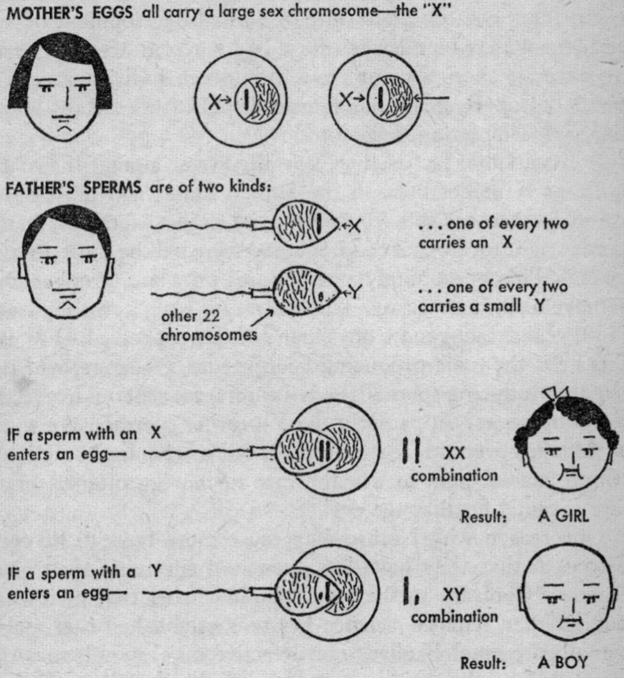

MOTHER'S EGGS all carry a large sex chromosome—the "X"

X

X

FATHER'S SPERMS are of two kinds:

X

. . . one of every two carries an X

Y

. . . one of every two carries a small Y

other 22 chromosomes

IF a sperm with an X enters an egg—

XX combination

Result: A GIRL

IF a sperm with a Y enters an egg—

XY combination

Result: A BOY

in the two X's throw the development of the baby towards femaleness. But when a Y chromosome enters the egg, its own maleness genes and those in the other chromosomes can predominate and cause the baby to develop as a boy.

Can a baby's sex be changed during the period before birth! No, once the baby has begun to develop as a boy, it cannot be turned into a girl, nor can a developing girl foetus be turned into a boy. (Even more impossible are the claims that mature men have been or could be transformed into women by 'operations' or treatments.) However, once in a thousand times, something may happen in prenatal life to throw sexual development from its proper course, and a boy may result whose sex organs are so incompletely developed that he may be mistaken for a girl; or a girl with abnormal development of her sex organs may be mistaken for a boy. Only in extremely rare instances is there a completely in-between individual who is neither properly male nor female. (For further details about this, see Chapter 13, page 109.)

A remarkable fact is that year after year, among the many millions of babies born in the United States and most other countries, there is an excess of boys by almost exactly the same percentage: for every 100 girls born, there will be close to 106 boys.* This is definitely not because boys are stronger and achieve birth more easily. The contrary is true, as we shall see. It is because many more boys than girls are conceived. How can this be if the male-producing sperms (the Y-bearers) and the female-producing sperms (the X-bearers) are sent out in exactly equal numbers? Apparently the Y-bearing sperms have some advantages over the X-sperms in speed or chemical reactions, which enable them to win the race to the egg oftener, or to more readily fertilize the egg.

One reason why Nature may cause more boys to be conceived is that they have less chance of surviving than have females. Contrary to the long-standing belief that males are hardier than females, science has now established that males actually are much likelier to be defective, and less able to withstand bad conditions than are females. This applies to every stage of life, but is most significant in the prenatal stages, when the environment for males and females is the same. Among the babies miscarried in the first few months the males outnumber the females by about two to one; and among those dying shortly before or immediately after birth there are about 130

* In Britain, the ratio is 100 girls to 105·1 boys.

boys to 100 girls. Moreover, the risk of being abnormal or defective is much greater for boy babies. When added to this is the fact that in almost every stage of life thereafter the male death rate is markedly higher, there is a very good reason why more males should be needed at the start.

Although the ratio among all babies born each year averages out close to 106 boys to 100 girls, the chances of having a boy may be above or below this average for mothers of different groups, ages, and physical conditions. Because boy foetuses are weaker, the general rule seems to be that where prenatal conditions are best, there is a greater chance for boy babies to achieve birth. Thus, among the more favoured groups there may possibly be up to 115 boys born for every 100 girls; in underprivileged groups, the ratio of boy to girl babies may be 103 or less. Moreover, in each group the healthiest young mothers, aged eighteen to twenty-two, have the greatest chance of producing boys – especially when it is the *first birth* – while among mothers aged thirty-eight to forty-two and over, the chances of having a boy may be less than even. Again, since male foetuses suffer more under unfavourable pre-birth conditions, it is not surprising that the more crowded the womb, the less are the relative chances that males will survive. In twin births the ratio drops to 103·5 boys to 100 girls; in triplets, 98 boys to 100 girls; in quadruplets, 70 boys to 100 girls.

There is a long-standing belief that the ratio of boys born goes up during and immediately after wars, perhaps because Nature is trying to help make up for the men killed off. The evidence for World Wars I and II supports this only slightly. After World War I an increase of from 1 to 2·5 per cent in the boy ratio was reported in some countries of Europe, but not in the United States. During World War II and its aftermath much smaller increases were reported. To the extent that any increases in the boy ratio occur, scientists ascribe it not to mysterious influences, but to the fact that in the war periods there are relatively more first births, and more babies born to the younger, healthier mothers whose chance of having boys is above average.

With regard to individual families, where parents have three or four children all of the same sex, this may easily be as much a matter of chance as tossing coins and having them turn up three or four heads in a row. But where one finds families with up to twelve sons and no daughters (or vice versa), and families heavily slanted for several generations towards children of one sex, the possibility arises that hereditary influences may be at work. The only real evidence in this direction comes from experiments with lower animals, in which strains have been bred with tendencies to produce much higher than average ratios of either males or females, as desired. While no such breeding has taken place among humans, it is not unlikely that in some families or individuals there also are inborn tendencies which would favour the production of offspring of one sex rather than the other. These tendencies might work directly through stronger sex genes of either type carried in the sperms or eggs, or indirectly through special factors in the environment of the mother's womb. But all of this still is theoretical so far as human beings are concerned.

As to sex-determining methods, in recent years much publicity has been given to one 'scientific method' or another for helping parents to have a baby of the sex they desire. As stated at the outset, none of these methods has proved to be effective. This applies, for example, to the acid-alkali treatment (acid for a girl, alkali for a boy). Also unproved is the theory that a boy is more likely to result if the mother conceives in the latter part of her fertile period. But scientists do believe that, eventually, means may be found of influencing the chances of having either a boy or a girl, as desired. Pointing to this are recent findings which indicate that the X-bearing and Y-bearing sperms differ in the size and shape of their heads, and perhaps also in chemical workings. Thus, possible future methods of sex control may include: (1) Separating the father's Y-bearing from the X-bearing sperms in a laboratory, and inseminating the mother with the desired type; or (2) injecting chemical preparations in the mother which will have different effects on the boy-producing or girl-producing sperms.

It may also be distinctly possible soon – if not already possible by the time you read this book – for parents to know the sex of an expected baby months before its birth. Differences in the types of hormones produced by a boy foetus, as compared with a girl foetus, or in other chemical reactions, may show up in tests of the mother. Also, recently reported by Israeli scientists and others, a sample of cells of the foetus itself, if obtainable from the amniotic fluid, can reveal the expected baby's sex.

So far in this chapter we have been speaking in terms of general averages as applied to millions of births each year. In your own case, with very few children involved, or with your mind on a single baby, the results may easily be different from the general odds. While it remains true that young, healthy mothers tend to produce more sons than do equal numbers of older, less healthy mothers, the reader (or the reader's wife) may be a young, healthy woman and yet have three or four girls and no boy; and a much older, sickly mother next door may have nothing but boys. Nor will the fact that you have had three girls, or three boys in a row, increase the chance that the next will be of the opposite sex. However, it is worth noting that the emphasis on having a child of one specific sex is becoming less marked in most advanced countries, particularly in the United States, where a growing number of parents see equal advantages in having girls or boys.

Do the sex genes stop working at birth? No, they continue to influence the sexual development of the body and its functioning throughout life. In the normal male the predominant maleness genes and the processes they set in motion will direct the production at the prescribed stages of all the many special masculine physical traits and functions – male sex organs, sex glands, and sperm production, bigger and heavier bones and muscles, beard, etc. In the female the stronger balance of femaleness genes will direct the development of all her many special physical characteristics and functions – her sex organs and glands, egg production, menstruation, preparation for childbearing and nursing, and the various distinguishing characteristics of her body as compared with that of the male. (In later chapters we shall also see how the sex genes affect the types and incidences of diseases and defects in males and females.) Although environmental factors are also constantly at work, the sex genes largely dictate when puberty begins, when sexual development reaches its fullest point, when child-bearing capacities in women cease, etc., as well as influencing many aspects of the behaviour in the two sexes.

CHAPTER FIVE

TWINS, 'TRIPS', 'QUADS', 'QUINTS'

THE FIRST THING to know about twins is whether they are 'identicals' or 'fraternals'. Confusion may create many difficulties in rearing twins, in their adjustment to each other, and in medical diagnosis of their ailments.

Identical twins are the one-egg twins, who are products of the same single egg and the same single sperm. These twins result when what started out to be a single baby becomes *two* babies by a splitting of the fertilized egg at a very early stage. In the process each twin gets duplicates of exactly the same chromosomes and genes, so that both have *identical heredity*. For this reason, also, identical twins *must always be of the same sex*, either two boys or two girls. But even though identical twins have exactly the same genes (and with respect to their hereditary factors are actually the same person in duplicate), their environments in the womb and after they are born may be different enough to keep them from ever being exactly the same in appearance, health, and behaviour. Sometimes these differences are quite marked. Usually, however, it is hard to tell identical twins apart, and frequently their remarkable similarities continue until the end of their lives.

Fraternal twins are the two-egg twins, products of two different eggs and two different sperms. They make up the majority of the twins – about 70 per cent. (That is, of all twins born, more than two out of three pairs are fraternals.) Even though fraternal twins are carried in the womb and born together, they need be no more alike than any two children of a family who are born separately. In about half the cases fraternal twins are different in sex; one in four times both are boys, one in four times both are girls. Fraternal twins just happen to be conceived at about the same time, when a mother produces two eggs instead of the usual one, and each egg is fertilized by a different sperm. (In rare instances one of a pair of fraternal twins may be conceived several days, or even a week or more, after the other.)

Telling whether twins are identical or fraternal is not always easy, and mistakes are often made (although not nearly as much so as in the past). At birth one cannot go by the old theory that if like-sexed twins have the same placenta and foetal sac, this proves they are identical, whereas the presence of different placentas and sacs proves they are fraternal. It is now known that in about one in four cases identical twins develop with separate placentas and sacs; conversely, in fraternal twins the sacs and placentas may sometimes be fused and appear to be one. Again, while generally true that twins who look remarkably alike are identicals, there are exceptions. Sometimes an early mishap or some unusual condition in the womb discriminating against one of an identical pair may cause him or her to look and be quite different from the other in various respects. On the other hand, just as two non-twin brothers or sisters may look remarkably alike, some fraternal twins also may look so much alike as to be mistaken for identicals.

To resolve doubts, a number of tests can now be made which will prove quite clearly if twins are fraternal or identical. The first test is for the blood types – A, B, O; Rh; M, N, etc. (explained in Chapter 15). If the twins have blood-type differences, this is immediate proof that they are *not* identicals. But should their blood types be the same, this still does not mean that they might not be a fraternal pair. Further clarifying tests may be for their similarities or dissimilarities in eye colour, eyesight, skin and hair colour; hair form; finger-, palm-, and footprints; blood pressure, pulse, respiration, brain-wave patterns; and various hereditary peculiarities or abnormalities. (In cases where the problem of twin diagnosis is complex, consult one of the heredity clinics or some medical geneticist. See Appendix.)

An unusual and special characteristic of identical twins is that any tissue from one can be successfully transplanted and take root in the body of the other. Even a whole organ, such as

How Twins Are Produced

IDENTICAL TWINS

—result from the same single egg and single sperm.

After the egg begins to grow it divides into equal halves with duplicated chromosomes.

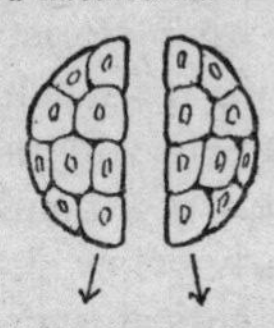

The halves go on to become two babies, with exactly the same hereditary factors.

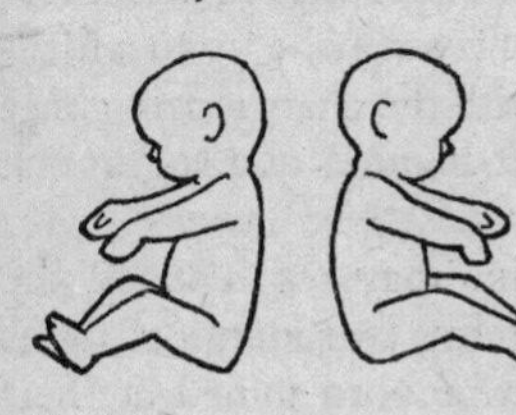

IDENTICAL twins are always the same sex (either two boys or two girls). They usually look much alike. They have exactly the same eye color, hair color, hair form, blood types and all other hereditary traits.

FRATERNAL TWINS

—result from two different eggs, fertilized by two different sperms.

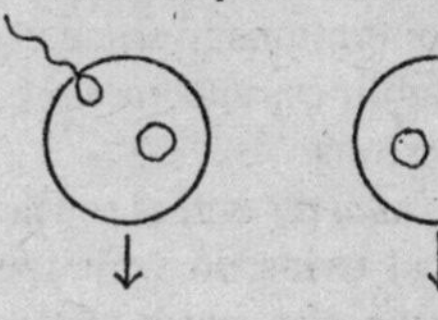

The two different fertilized eggs develop separately into two different embryos.

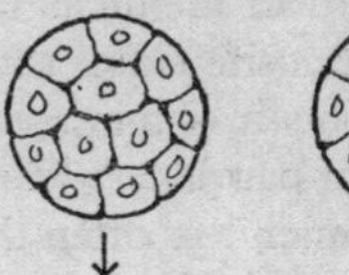

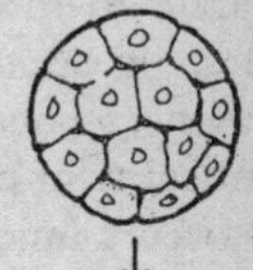

The two embryos grow into two babies with different hereditary factors.

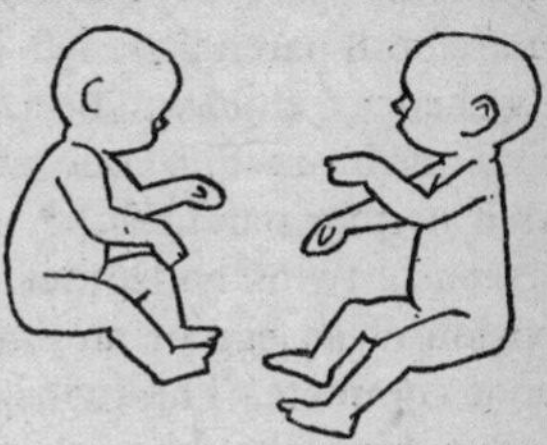

FRATERNAL twins may be either of the same sex (two boys or two girls), or different in sex (a boy and a girl). They may be different in looks, coloring, hair form, blood types, and other hereditary traits.

a kidney, has been successfully transplanted from one identical twin to another in many cases. But between non-identical twins, as between any two genetically different persons, a transplant will normally 'take' only temporarily. However, recent medical techniques have made possible organ-transplanting operations in some cases even between fraternal twins, or other siblings, and in time may be carried out between unrelated persons.

Mirror-imaging refers to the peculiarity, in about 30 per cent of identical twins, in which a birthmark, or some oddity in a tooth, feature, or organ of the body, appears on the right side of one twin and the left side of another. Such reverse patterning results from the fact that when the halves of the same embryo separate to form identical twins, certain characteristics may appear on opposite sides, somewhat as with the cut halves of an apple. This in some instances may explain why one of an identical twin pair is left-handed, the other right-handed. But this occurs much less often than is popularly believed. In fact, the incidence of left-handedness among identical twins (about 10 per cent) is only a little higher than among fraternal twins, or even among persons in the general population.

Whether among twins or singly born persons, heredity may play some part in the tendency towards left-handedness. Where both parents are left-handed, there may be up to a fifty-fifty chance a child will be a 'leftie', with the chance being only about one in six if just one parent is left-handed, and very much less if neither parent is.

Siamese twins and other freak twins may result when the division of an egg or an embryo forming two identical twins is not complete. The twins may then be born joined at their breasts, hips, shoulders or heads. (The famed circus pair from Siam from whom the name derives were joined at the hip.) It is estimated that Siamese twins occur about once in 50,000 births. Few of these twins survive into maturity. In the past, operations to separate Siamese twins usually failed, but in recent years improved operative techniques have led to a number of successful separations. The worst freaks are those in whom the early embryonic separation is only partial, resulting in monsters with two heads and one body, or one body and four arms and four legs, etc. Most of these, fortunately, die before birth.

The *incidence* of twins varies greatly among different races and groups, and among individual mothers within any group. Racially, the highest twinning rate is among Negroes, the lowest among Japanese and other Mongolian peoples, with the rates among whites being in a range in between. In the United States, in the years 1956, 1957, and 1958, the incidence among whites was about one twin pair in 100 births, and among Negroes, one in 73. In European countries twinning incidences average about one pair in 90 to 95 births, with such variations as one in 70 in Denmark, one in 80 in England and one in 110 in Spain. The world record for twinning is believed held by the Yoruba Negroes of Nigeria, with a reported rate as high as one twin pair in 25 births.

In any given group, the age of the mother plays a big part in her twinning chances. On the average, older mothers have a much greater chance of bearing twins than have younger mothers, this being further affected by the number of children a mother has had previously. Thus, a mother in her mid- or late thirties with five or six previous children, may have six times the chance of producing twins as a mother under twenty in her first pregnancy.

In all cases, the differences in twinning chances apply almost entirely to fraternal twins. With regard to identicals, the rates are virtually the same – about 3·5 to 4 identical pairs per 1,000 births – among all races. But the incidences of fraternal twins vary enormously, ranging from averages of a little over 2 per 1,000 among the Japanese, to 6 to 8 per 1,000 among whites, and 10 or more among Negroes, reaching possibly up to 30 or more per 1,000 in some African tribes. Similarly, the big differences in twinning chances of older mothers as compared with younger mothers, previously noted, are due almost entirely to the fact that an older mother is far more likely to produce fraternal twins in a given pregnancy, although her chance of having identical twins is only a little greater than that of the young mother.

Just as the racial differences in twinning appear to be much influenced by heredity, there also are strong indications that the twinning chances of individual mothers in any race or group also are influenced by heredity. Repeated sets of twins occur in many families, in some cases five or six to a single mother. Once a mother has borne twins it also has been shown that her chances of a repeat twin birth are several times that of a mother who hasn't had twins before. The extent to which twins are found among a couples' close relatives also affects their chances of having twins. In general, perhaps one in every four or five women is believed to have a special tendency to produce twins.

How heredity works in producing a predisposition towards twinning is still uncertain. It would have to be different for the two types of twinning. For producing identical twins, the genes may be ones which stimulate an egg to split at an early stage. For fraternal twins, the genes may stimulate the mother's ovaries to produce two eggs at a time instead of one. A further indication is that any twinning genes there are would come from both parents, or through their parents, so that the father, as well as the mother, would have something to do with the production of twins. But in all cases, an important factor is whether, once twins are conceived, a given mother can safely carry them through to birth. Undoubtedly, many more twins are conceived than the number who begin to develop and make their presence known.

Most of the general facts regarding two-at-a-time babies apply to the *supertwins* – triplets, quadruplets and, the rarest, quintuplets. The distinctions between identicals and fraternals also hold for the higher multiples, with the difference that since more than two are involved, one may find among the supertwins combinations of both identicals and fraternals, as well as all of one type or the other. Thus, all may be identicals – products of a single fertilized egg; or all may be fraternals – each from a different egg; or there may be a mixed identical and fraternal set. For example, in triplets, all may have come from the same egg, and thus be identicals; or two may be identicals, derived from one egg, and the third a fraternal, from a second egg. Similarly, among quadruplets and quintuplets, all members of a set may come from the same egg and be identicals; or they may come from two or more eggs, and be a combination of identicals and fraternals; or they may each come from a different egg, and be an all-fraternal set. Differences in sexes further increase the range of possible combinations in supertwin sets.

The world-famous Dionne quintuplets, born in Canada in 1934 (the first recorded quintuplet set in which all five survived, and who remained as a unit until Emilie's death in 1954), were definitely proved to be an all-identical set, derived from the same single fertilized egg. The Diligentis of Argentina, who were reported as a quintuplet set only some time after their birth in 1943, consisted of three boys and two girls. While their relationship has not been clearly established, there is some indication that they may have derived either from three eggs or four eggs.

The incidences of supertwins, in relation to twins and single births, seems to be governed by a remarkable natural formula. Known as 'Hellin's law' (after its German discoverer, D. Hellin), this formula provides that the incidence of triplets will be the square of the ratio of twins to single births; of quadruplets, the cube of the incidence of twins; of quintuplets, the fourth power of the incidence of twins. Thus, if twins occur once in 90 births, triplets should occur once in 90 × 90, or 8,100 births; quadruplets, once in 90 × 90 × 90, or 729,000 births; quintuplets, once in the latter number by 90 again, or 65,610,000 births. Actual supertwin incidences in the United States and other countries have come fairly close to this formula, but how it operates is still to be fully explained.

A remaining question is why scientists have given so much study to twins. If you yourself have a set of twins (or trips, or quads!), you will soon find that geneticists, doctors, and psychologists are much interested in them. The study of twins offers some of the most important clues as to the degree in which human traits are hereditary or environmental. For instance, since identical twins carry exactly the same genes, any differences between them must be due to environment, whether before or after birth. This applies to differences in stature, body-build, features, or health, as well as to differences in IQ, behaviour, achievement, and personality. The greater the difference in any trait between identical twins, the more strongly it points to the role of environment in helping to produce that trait. On the other hand, where identical twins are raised in very different environments, as in cases of those separated in infancy and reared by different foster parents, remarkable similarities may yet appear in their physical makeup, diseases, and defects, and often in mental qualities and capacities. These similarities offer evidence of the role of heredity. Finally, when identical twins are compared with fraternal twins, the relative degrees of similarity or difference between paired twins of the two types may offer important clues to as the comparative influences of heredity and environment. (Twin studies will be dealt with again at various later points in this book. See Index for specific references.)

CHAPTER SIX

PREDICTING CHILDREN'S LOOKS

PEOPLE WONDER WHAT their children will look like for more reasons than mere curiosity. Individuals are flattered when their children resemble them (at least in the desirable aspects) and relatives may be partial to the child who is most like them or their side of the family. Of most concern is that the child – particularly if a girl – be good-looking. On the latter point, fortunately, the chances that a daughter will be pretty or a son handsome are much greater today than ever before in most countries. The genes for looks have not changed, but environments have. Great improvements in diet, health, living conditions, and medical and dental care are steadily helping to produce better-looking, better-built, and taller young people, and very few grow up to be really 'homely'.

If human beings were bred as are cats, dogs, or blooded livestock, predictions regarding the looks of an expected child would be easy. Through many successive generations of controlled breeding of domesticated animals, the genes of particular breeds have been so selected and fixed that there is little doubt about the size, shape, colouring, and feature details of offspring of a given mating. But human beings have at no time been bred so deliberately. Every person today is a descendant of a great many ancestors of varied types, and carries a haphazard collection of hundreds of genes governing body structure and outward appearance. Many of these genes reveal themselves by the surface traits they produce. But many other genes may have their effects suppressed in the parents, though they can assert themselves in a child. It is in the latter way that various unexpected and sometimes baffling traits may appear in children.

Any forecast of what the expected children of a given couple will look like is largely a matter of knowing or guessing what genes for the traits in question the parents carry, and then estimating the chances that their children will inherit the gene combinations required to produce these traits. If the parents are fairly similar in colouring and important features, and are of the same ethnic and/or racial stocks, they are likely to be carrying many matching genes for the traits they themselves show. Their children, then, are apt to inherit gene combinations which will make them resemble not only their parents, but their brothers and sisters, in many details. But when the parents are very different in colouring and features, and are of different stocks, their children can inherit any of numerous gene combinations. In such cases it is possible for a child to look not only unlike the parents, but unlike other children in the family. However, conclusions about this cannot be drawn until maturity, because family resemblances often come out and increase with age.

With respect to many traits that given couples show, geneticists can say there is an almost 100 per cent chance that these will reappear in their children. But there are many other traits where the expectancy of appearance in children can be stated only in terms of odds, such as a 'one-in-two chance', or a 'one-in-four chance', or even more reduced chances. All of such fractional forecasts are based on the knowledge of how the genes for a given trait work according to the principles of *dominance* and *recessiveness*, explained in Chapter 3 (the 'Mendelian laws'). Here are some of the possibilities of transmission.

1. If either parent has a dominant trait (such as dark eyes) and the other parent has the corresponding recessive trait (such as blue eyes), there is at best a fifty-fifty chance any child will show the recessive trait. This will depend on whether the parent with the dominant trait is also carrying a hidden recessive gene for the trait. But if this parent is not carrying the recessive gene, every child will show the dominant trait.

2. If both parents have a given dominant trait (such as dark eyes or dark hair), there is at best only a one-in-four chance a child will show the corresponding recessive trait (such as light-coloured eyes or blond hair). This can happen only if each

parent is carrying a hidden recessive gene for the trait, paired with the dominant gene, and the two recessive genes come together in a child. Obviously, if both parents carry only dominant genes for a trait, there is no chance a child will show the recessive trait.

3. If both parents show a recessive trait (blue eyes, blond hair, etc.) which means neither is carrying the corresponding dominant gene, every child will show the recessive trait. (Rare exceptions will be dealt with in later chapters.)

The 'looks' genes often do not work according to simple formulas. There are some genes that may produce particular effects only if they are coupled with unidentified other genes, or only if there are certain special factors in the environment. In such cases the odds for the appearance of the trait in question may be uncertain, and one may speak of inheritance in terms such as 'probable', 'possible', 'not too likely', etc.

Among the unexpected results may be that two very handsome parents sometimes have a child who is definitely not good-looking. If this is not because of some prenatal condition, or some disease, accident, or other environmental factor, heredity may be involved in this way: Each of the good-looking parents could be carrying recessive genes which, coming together in a child, would produce homely features. Fortunately, a much more common situation these days is for two homely parents to have a very good-looking child. This, again, may be for two reasons: (1) Bad environmental conditions in the parents' childhood may have kept them from becoming as good-looking as their genes would have permitted. With more favourable environments today the same genes would make their children better looking. Or (2) each parent could be carrying genes which in new combinations with the genes from the other parent would produce better looks. (See chart, page 52).

Whenever fractional odds are given that a child or children will or may inherit some trait, the reader should bear in mind that these odds are only in terms of averages. The results in the case of a single child or a single family need be no more

HOW TWO HOMELY PARENTS MAY HAVE A BEAUTIFUL CHILD

FATHER

Bald

Murky-green eyes; lashes lost through disease

Misshapen mouth due to bad teeth

Bad nose due to accident

MOTHER

Dull, dark straight hair.

Dull-brown eyes; drooping eyelids

Bad skin (local disorder)

Protruding under-lip

BUT they may carry and pass on to their child hidden genes for

—Blond, curly hair
Blue eyes
Long lashes
Pretty nose
Cupid's-bow mouth
Lovely complexion

RESULT: A "BEAUTY CONTEST" WINNER

HOW TWO HANDSOME PARENTS MAY HAVE A HOMELY CHILD

FATHER

Curly, black hair

Large, dark eyes, long lashes

Well-shaped mouth and chin

MOTHER

Wavy, blond hair

Blue eyes, long lashes

Regular teeth, pretty mouth

BUT they may carry and pass on to their child hidden genes for

—Dull-brown, straight hair
Murky-green, small eyes with short lashes
Protruding jaw and teeth
Other irregularities, added to by environmental factors

RESULT: AN "UGLY DUCKLING"

certain than the results in any game or venture where chance is involved. For instance, if a parent carries a dominant gene for a trait, paired with a recessive gene, the chance that a child will get one or the other is like tossing up a coin. On the average the chances for heads or tails are exactly even. But sometimes one may get three or four heads in a row, and sometimes a run of tails. Likewise, when we say there is a fifty-fifty chance that a child will show a given inherited trait, it is possible in the case of a particular family that this trait may turn up in two or three, or even four children in a row, or in none at all. (This is similar to the situation with regard to the chances of having boys or girls, discussed in Chapter 4.) Again, if we say there is a one-in-four chance that a recessive trait may appear, it is possible that in one four-child family, two or three children may have the trait, whereas in another four-child, or even six- or seven-child family, no one will have it.

One important point that many persons find hard to accept is that the stated odds for the appearance of any trait *remain the same for each successive child* in a family, regardless of what has happened with the others. Again it is like tossing coins: if the chances are fifty-fifty for a head or a tail, one may toss three heads in a row, and there will still be the same fifty-fifty chance that the next toss will bring a head or a tail. So if first-time parents are told there is an even chance they will have a blond baby, and their baby is dark-haired, the chance for their second baby's being blond is again no greater or no less than fifty-fifty. Only when one checks the results with large numbers of children does one find that the predicted genetic odds work out very closely.

CHAPTER SEVEN

COLOURING: EYES AND HAIR

HUMAN BEINGS ARE much less gaudily or variably coloured than are a great many, if not most, species of other animals, and the human colouring processes are generally simpler. In fact, all the colours of eyes, hair, and skin found among human beings of every type and race are produced in much the same way and with the same few basic pigments. The main pigment, or colouring ingredient, is *melanin*, a brownish substance. The amount and strength of this colouring matter, and the way it is distributed, is the chief factor in making eyes, hair, or skin darker or lighter. In addition to melanin there are several other pigments that produce special colour effects. How the colouring process works in given individuals is determined largely by the activity of the colour genes they inherit, although various environmental factors can modify the results.

Eye colour depends mainly on how the basic pigment, melanin, is distributed in the *iris*, the disclike part of the eye with the pupil at its centre. The less pigment there is in the iris, the lighter the eye; the more pigment, the darker. As to particular eye colours, they are not produced by different coloured pigments (like painted objects), but are mostly the *effects* of the way the same melanin pigment is concentrated in the eye, and how it reflects the light. In *blue* eyes, for instance, there is no blue pigment in the iris, but the blue effect results only from the way the light is reflected back to the viewer by the pigment particles in the rear of the iris – just as the sky is made to appear blue through an optical effect. In *grey* or *grey-blue* eyes, some extra pigment is distributed in the front of the iris in such a way as to give the greyish effect. In *green* eyes a special scattering of yellow pigment (possibly diluted melanin) in the front of the iris converts the bluish effect into green (somewhat in the way that yellow dots stippled on blue produce a greenish effect). Different amounts of light-brown or yellow pigment in the iris, and different patterns of pigment distribution, produce the various other light eye colours. The darker eyes, ranging from *brown* to *black*, result from the heaviest concentrations of pigment. (See illustration, page 56.)

Although the inheritance of eye colour is often complex, the main results usually are determined by a few key genes. A 'strong' eye-pigment gene produces dark eyes. 'Weak' eye-pigment genes produce the lighter-coloured eyes. Should a child receive a strong gene from one parent, a weak gene from the other, the stronger gene will dominate and the child will have dark eyes (with only occasional exceptions). To have blue eyes, or any other lighter-coloured eyes (light grey, light brown, green) a child must therefore get weaker colour genes from both parents. When the parents have light eyes of different colours, the tendency is for the blue gene to be dominated by the light brown, grey, or green genes, although it is quite possible that the non-blue-eyed parent may also be carrying hidden genes for blue eyes, and that the child will have blue eyes. Some shades and gradations of eye colour may be influenced by structural details of the eye, iris patterns, blood vessels in the eye, chemical influences in the body, and the state of the person's health.

True *albino* eyes have no pigment in them whatsoever. The 'pinkness' of these eyes results from the tiny blood vessels in the otherwise colourless iris, and the reflection from other blood vessels inside the eye. The absence of eye pigment is due to a pair of abnormal genes that also interfere with the colouring processes of the hair and skin. (Further details on albinism and its inheritance are given in later chapters.)

In occasional instances a person may have one eye dark and the other light, or each eye of a different shade or colour. This condition (*heterochromia iridis*) may result in several ways, and sometimes heredity may be involved. For example: (1) A person may inherit one brown-eye gene and one blue-eye gene. Normally this would produce brown eyes, but if in an early embryonic stage the brown-eye gene is knocked out of action on one side of the face, the blue-eye gene may take over on that side, producing a blue eye, whereas the other eye with its brown gene working as usual becomes brown. (2) In an embryo with light-eye genes something may happen to increase pigment production abnormally in one of the eyes, causing it

Eye Colours

All eye colours are effects of how genes work to produce pigment deposits in the iris

BLUE EYES

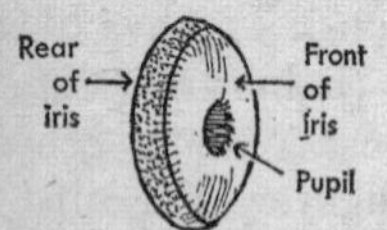

Light deposit of pigment in rear of iris, but not in front. "Blue" is only an optical effect. (See text.)

GRAY EYES

Light pigmentation in rear, as in blue eyes, but also some scattered dark pigment in front, which "grays down" the blue effect.

GREEN EYES

Rear of iris pigmented as in blue eyes, but scattered yellow pigment in front: Yellow over blue effect gives the green hue.

BROWN EYES

Heavy deposit of pigment in rear of iris, and also some pigment in front.

BLACK EYES

Very heavy deposit of pigment in both rear and front of the iris.

ALBINO EYES

No pigment at all in iris —"pink" effect due to reflection of blood vessels inside.

to become much darker, or different in colour, from the other. (3) While either of the foregoing situations may be purely environmental, it is also possible for an inherited abnormality to produce unmatched eyes. The condition, either dominant or recessive, runs in some human families, but is much more common among cats, dogs, rabbits, and other animals.

'Tortoise-shell' eyes (mottled yellow and black) and 'ruby' eyes are among other rare types found in individuals. They may possibly occur through mutations in the eye-colour genes.

While most persons' eyes remain the same in basic colour throughout life, it should not be overlooked that eye colours are capable of being modified by inherent chemical changes, ageing effects, and various environmental factors. At birth most white babies (and many Negro babies) have slate-blue eyes, which in some may presently become heavily pigmented, turning brown, and in others may turn clear blue, depending on the types of genes they received. Sometimes a child's true eye colour does not become set until it is several years old, and often there is a change at puberty. Diseases or nutritional deficiencies may affect eye-pigment production, leading to either darkening or lightening. Cataracts may make dark eyes bluish, as may ageing effects.

The facts given in preceding sections, and in those which follow, should enable most prospective parents to make fairly accurate guesses as to what the eye colours of their children will be – or, at least, what the odds are that given types of eye colour will appear in them.

Both parents dark-eyed: All children will probably have dark eyes – *unless each mate* has some light-eyed close blood relative (particularly one of his or her parents, or a brother or sister), in which case there is a chance (but no more than one in four) of having a light-eyed child (blue-, grey-, or green-eyed). Only rarely do two dark-eyed parents with no known light-eyed blood relatives produce a light-eyed child, but it can happen. Once two dark-eyed parents have had a light-eyed child, there is a one-in-four chance of having another or others.

One mate dark-eyed, the other light-eyed: If the dark-eyed mate has no light-eyed close blood relative, there is little more chance of the couple's having a light-eyed child than if both mates are dark-eyed. (See preceding section.) But if the dark-eyed mate does have one or more light-eyed relatives (particularly a parent) there is up to a one-in-two chance of producing a light-eyed child or children in conjunction with the light-eyed mate.

Both mates light-eyed: It is about 98 per cent certain each is carrying only light-eye genes, and that all their children will be light-eyed. Should both mates be blue-eyed, their children will have approximately the same eye colour. But if the eyes of one or both parents are green, grey, or very light brown, a child's eyes may be any one of these colours, or blue. But no child's eyes in a mating between two light-eyed parents are apt to be much darker than the eyes of either parent. However, in about 2 per cent of the cases this may happen if one of the parents is carrying a hidden dark-eye gene which for some complex reason failed to assert itself. (The fact that a wife and husband are blue-eyed, and that a dark-eyed child is born to them, is therefore by no means proof that the child is not legitimate. See Chapter 28, page 247.)

Hair-colour inheritance follows the same principles as eye-colour inheritance. The degrees of darkness in hair depend on how strong or active the hair-pigment genes are, mainly with respect to how much of the basic brown pigment, melanin, they produce. In black hair the hair cells are heavily filled with melanin, in brown hair there is less, in light, blond hair there is very little; and in white hair virtually none. Special hair-colour effects may result from the addition of other pigments (as in red hair). Shades of the same hair colour may be influenced by the way the hair cells are constructed, their oiliness or dryness, changes in the body chemistry, and other factors, in all of which hereditary tendencies, as well as environmental influences, play a part. In children, light hair tends to darken somewhat with puberty, blond hair often becoming brown; while in later ages, of course, hair may become lighter through the weakened action of the pigment genes and changes in the hair cells. (Natural grey hair, and premature grey hair, are due to special factors to be discussed later.) All of the various influences on hair colour must be taken into account in tracing hair-colour inheritance in any family.

As is also true in eye colour, the strongest and most active hair-colour genes almost always dominate the weaker ones, so that if a person inherits a dark-hair gene from one parent, a light-hair gene from the other, the hair will be dark. For the same reason, a dark-haired person may often be carrying a hidden gene for any of the lighter hair shades, but a fair-haired person cannot be carrying a dark-hair gene (except in rare instances).

The Hair-Colour Genes

All human hair-colour differences are due mainly to how genes work to deposit the basic brownish pigment, melanin, among the hair cells.

BLOND HAIR

Dilute melanin pigment gives yellowish effect. The less the pigment, the lighter the shade of blond.

RED HAIR

A special gene works to produce red pigment, diffused with scattered melanin pigment.

BROWN HAIR

Heavy deposit of pigment. The more pigment, the darker the shade of brown.

BLACK HAIR

Extremely heavy deposit of melanin-pigment granules.

NOTE: Various internal and external influences can modify the effects of the hair-color genes. See text.

Red hair results from special genes, which produce a reddish pigment. The degree to which the red shows through depends on the activity of the other hair-colour genes the person carries. When coupled with a gene for black hair, the effects of the red genes will be obscured. But when the red-hair genes are coupled with genes for lighter hair shades, the results may be reddish-gold, chestnut, or vividly red hair. The red-hair genes are found in all racial groups, including pure Negroes, among whom red hair sometimes appears when their dark-hair genes are not strongly active. (See also last paragraph of this chapter.)

White hair can be due to several causes: (1) defective genes (as in albinos), which prevent the production of any pigment in the hair cells; (2) very weak blond-hair genes, which produce almost no pigment; (3) diseases, hereditary or environmental, which interfere with the hair-pigmenting process; or (4) ageing affects. In the latter case, the approximate stage in a person's life when his hair begins to grey and then turns white is often governed by heredity, with the greying taking place in some families much earlier than others. While nerve disorders, diseases, or shocks may affect hair cells and the hair-pigmentation process, causing new hair to grow out white, it is a myth that a person's whole head of hair can turn white overnight.

In most cases very dark eyes and very dark hair go together, almost invariably so among pure Negroes and Mongolians. But among whites it is not uncommon to see a person with very dark hair and blue or light-grey eyes, or, conversely, blond hair and dark eyes. Among mulattos and other racially mixed persons, also, dark-light combinations in eyes and hair (or vice versa) are seen. This is proof that the eye-colour and hair-colour genes may be inherited separately and work independently.

In trying to guess what an expected child's hair colour will be, parents must first seek to determine what hair-colour genes they carry. They can be guided in this by being clear as to the *natural* colour of their hair, ruling out any changes produced artificially or by acquired diseases (which can have had no effect on their genes); by what their own hair colour was in childhood and at puberty; and by types and shades of hair colour in their parents, brothers and sisters, and other close relatives. With these facts in mind, the following general forecasts may be made:

Both parents dark-haired: All children will most probably have dark hair – *unless each parent* has some light-haired close blood relative or relatives (or is otherwise carrying a hidden light-hair gene), in which case there is a chance – but no more than one in four – of having a light-haired child. In any case once a dark-haired couple has had a fair-haired child, there is a one-in-four chance of having another or others.

One mate dark-haired, other light-haired: If the dark-haired mate has no light-haired close blood relative, which strongly indicates he or she is carrying only dark-hair genes, there is little more chance of the couple's having a light-haired child than if both parents were dark-haired. (See preceding section.) But if the dark-haired mate does have one or more fair-haired close relatives (particularly a parent), there is up to a one-in-two chance of producing a fair-haired child in conjunction with the light-haired mate.

Both parents brown-haired: Most children's hair will be brown, possibly a little darker or lighter than the parents', and with a chance that some child may be blond.

Both parents blond: Their children are almost certain to be blond (especially if the parents are light blond or flaxen-haired). But occasionally blond parents may produce a brown-haired child.

Red hair: Two true red-headed parents are likely to have all red-headed children, but light-brown or blond hair may also appear among their offspring. If one mate is red-headed, the other blond, there may be an even chance of having a red-headed child, with a reduced chance if the other parent is dark-haired. Redheads also appear sometimes when both mates are dark-haired, but only very rarely if both parents are blond.

CHAPTER EIGHT

SKIN COLOUR

WHILE THERE ARE marked differences in skin colour among individuals – especially of different races – we noted in the last chapter that all human beings have the same basic skin-colouring elements, although in varying proportions as governed by particular genes. Melanin is the chief skin-colouring pigment, as it is in eye- and hair-colouring. There are several additional skin pigments, among them melanoid and carotene (yellowish or yellowish-red), and several blood pigments in the skin that contribute to its colouring. Also influencing the skin colour of individuals is the structure of the skin and its thickness and oiliness, to which heredity may contribute. Environment can modify skin colour through such factors as exposure to the sun (to be discussed later), changes in the person's health, and age. But since the effects of environment cannot be inherited, the big differences in human colouring everywhere are those produced by the genes people inherit.

What chiefly determines a person's skin colour is the way that certain genes work to lay down deposits of the two brownish pigments, melanin and melanoid, in the skin cells. The relative amounts and strengths of these pigments, and how they are combined in persons, account for many grades of skin colour, from almost black through dark brown, light brown, and light. In other words, the most active melanin-melanoid genes are in the darkest Negroes, the least active in the 'whitest' whites. In addition, an especially active carotene gene contributes to the yellowish skin of Mongolians and the bronze skin of their relatives, the American Indians. However, the terms 'black', 'yellow', 'red', and 'white' to describe races are highly inexact, because few Negroes are really black, no Mongolians are really yellow, no Indians are red, and no whites are white. But more than this, some whites, such as are found in India and the Arab countries, have blacker skins than many Negroes (even of certain native African tribes).

In offspring of persons with markedly different skin colours there may appear to be a blending of the colours, but actually, the effects are only those of new combinations of the skin-colour genes. There is an important difference here from the way the eye-colour or hair-colour genes work. In producing eye colour, if a dark-eye gene is coupled with a light-eye gene, the dark-eye gene dominates the process (as we saw in the preceding chapter), and the child has dark eyes. The results with one dark-eye gene are virtually the same as with two dark-eye genes. (This is also true of combined dark and light hair-colour genes.) But in skin colour, if one dark-skin gene is coupled with one light-skin gene, there is no dominance of the first over the second. Instead there is an in-between result.

How the skin-colour genes work is best shown in the results of (1), a Negro–white mating, producing mulatto offspring; and (2), a mating between two mulattos. As indicated in the illustration, page 64, a pure Negro carries several pairs of dark-skin genes and a pure white several pairs of white-skin genes. (There are undoubtedly more than the two pairs shown for each.) In the first mating, each of the offspring receives one set of the Negro-skin genes, and one set of the white-skin genes, which produces in each much the same in-between skin-colour. But when two mulattos mate, their different skin colour genes sort out independently to form any of various combinations: One child may get *all* Negro-skin genes, and be as dark as the darkest Negro grandparent; another child may get *all* white-skin genes, and be as light as the lightest white grandparent; or a child may get any mixed combination of the genes, and have any skin colour in between these extremes. However, since the feature genes (which we will deal with in the next chapter) are also inherited separately, a child of two mulattos who has the lightest skin might have features that are much more Negroid than those of his darkest brother.

One of the most persistent popular myths is that two white

Skin Colour

IF A NEGRO MATES WITH A WHITE:

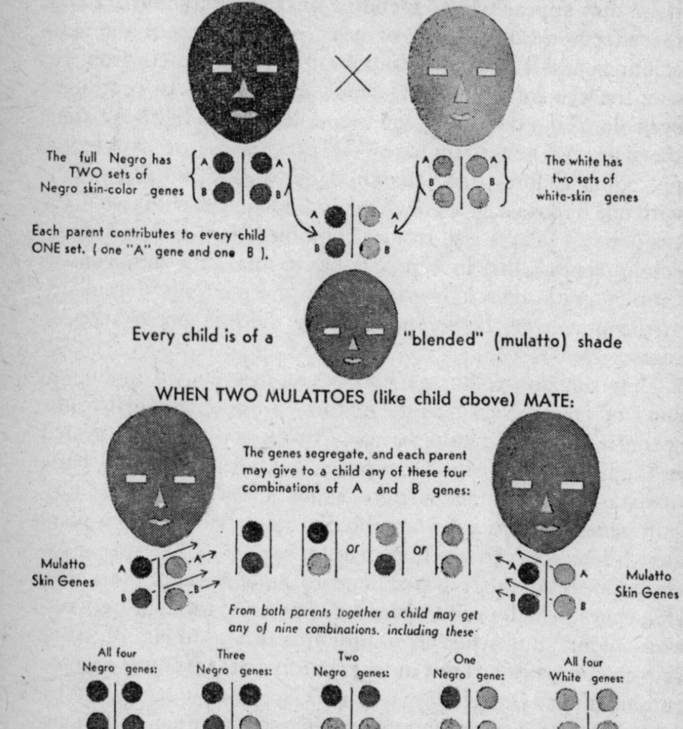

PRODUCING CHILDREN OF VARIOUS SHADES:

Black Dark Light White

(NOTE: *Only two types of skin color genes are shown, but there probably are more*)

(Adapted from *The New* YOU AND HEREDITY. Copyright, 1939, 1950, by Amram Scheinfeld.)

parents sometimes produce a coal-black baby if one of the parents has some long-hidden 'Negro blood'. This cannot really happen, first, because a very dark-skinned baby can be produced only if it receives Negro skin-colour genes from *both* parents; and second, if one parent alone carried skin-colour genes strong enough to make the baby 'black', that parent would not look white. Wherever these 'black-baby' cases have been tracked down, they are either found to be untrue, or else the parents involved were both racially mixed and may or may not have been passing as whites. Also, contrary to popular notions, there is probably less Negro–white mixing in the United States today than in former times, and the Negro population as a whole is not becoming lighter in skin colour. (See Chapter 27.)

How much influence does environment have, or has it had, on racial differences in skin colour? All that environment can do is to increase or decrease the *effects* of the skin-colour genes to a certain extent. Under a hot sun the pigmentation process is speeded up to lay down more pigment particles in the skin and thus give it added protection. This is what happens when a person tans during the summer. If a white man lives a long time in the tropics his skin may become very tanned, but no matter how dark it gets it will never look like true Negro skin. Nor will his children be born any less white than if he lived in Norway. Once the same white man leaves the tropics and remains away his skin will become progressively lighter. Pure Negroes, however, have much the same basic skin colour whether they live in Africa or in the United States, although those exposed continually to hot sun will be somewhat darker, everything else equal, than those who are not.

Even in Africa, as elsewhere, under the same conditions some strains of Negroes are always much darker than others. Nor need it be added that the dark skin of Negroes is due solely to the fact that they have inherited dark-skin genes, and not to centuries of exposure to the sun (as Shakespeare's Othello thought). Just as white children continue to be born to heavily tanned white parents in the tropics, dark Negro children continue to be born to Negroes who for generations have lived in northern American cities.

Heredity also plays a considerable part in the way different skins react to the sun. In some white persons the pigment genes will be quickly stirred to added activity under a hot sun, and they will tan easily and with no discomfort. Other persons – particularly fair-skinned redheads and those with 'milky-white' skins – will simply *broil.* But even some Negroes sun-burn painfully.

Because of the complexity of skin-colour inheritance, only a few general observations can be made other than those with respect to Negro-white or mulatto matings. Among whites, where one parent has darkish, swarthy skin (as in Italians, Arabians, and other Mediterranean peoples) and the other parent is fair-skinned, the children are likely to be of in-between shades. Again, if both parents are of mixed stock, each with some swarthy and some fair-skinned relatives, their children may also be any of these varied skin-colour types. Familial resemblances in skin colour are apt to become stronger with ageing.

The tendency to *freckling* often runs in families, with inheritance by way of a dominant gene. Transmission of freckling is especially likely where there is red hair, with which freckles are most often coupled.

CHAPTER NINE

THE FEATURES

MANY THINGS CAN make people look the way they do. Heredity, obviously, is almost the sole factor in making humans distinctive in every detail of their looks from all other animals. But it is the relatively minor differences in appearance among humans themselves that we have in mind when we speak of inheritance of features. As a rule, then, the genes set the pattern for the way individual characteristics in features develop in the growing child, the shapes they take at maturity, and the changes they undergo in later years. One of the clearest proofs of this is that identical twins, who have the same genes, preserve a remarkable resemblance to each other throughout life, even when living apart under different conditions.

However, environment can often do a great deal to modify the features, although much more, usually, with respect to their outer forms than to their inner construction. The changes in underlying fat, tissue and muscles of the face and its parts are what we chiefly notice when we remark upon the differences in a person's looks that result from disease, state of health, or age.

The feature genes, of which there are a great many, work together to shape both the face as a whole and its separate details. For instance, the shaping and appearance of the eyes will depend not only on the specific eye genes, but on the way other genes help to construct the brows, forehead, nose bridge, and cheekbones, and to lay down fatty tissue in the region. Other features are similarly influenced in their appearance by surrounding details.

Sex differences also have a big influence on the features. Although men and women inherit the same feature genes, the effects of these may be considerably modified in one direction or another by the basic sex differences in body chemistry.

Thus, just as the XY and XX sex-chromosome mechanisms cause the sex organs of males to develop differently from those of females, in a more limited way they also affect the features, causing males as a group to have relatively heavier brows, squarer chins, heavier facial muscles and more facial and body hair, and women to have softer facial contours and relatively smaller noses, ears, and mouths. (For sex differences in stature and body form, see next chapter.)

Shapes and appearances of persons' eyes result mainly from the way the key eye genes construct the eye sockets, eyeballs, and eyelids, as well as the surrounding bony structure of the face and their fleshy parts. Moreover, the width of the nose bridge has an important influence on the spacing between the eyes.

"Eye-Shape" Genes

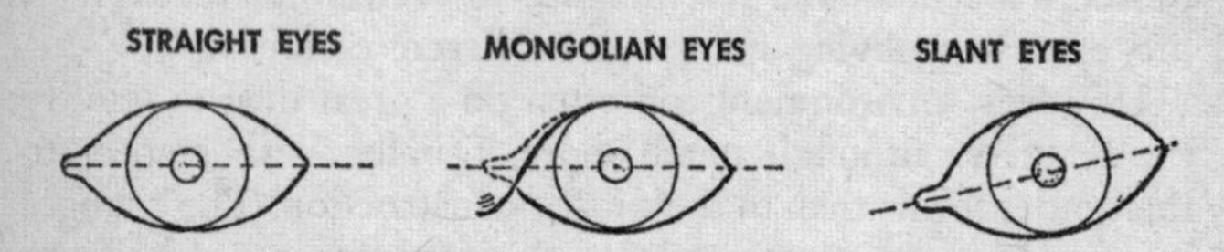

Note contrast between *true* slant eyes and the Mongolian, which only appear slanted because of overlapping inner eyelid fold (*epicanthus*). When mixed eye-shape genes are inherited, the gene for Mongolian dominates the straight-eye and slant-eye genes of whites; the straight-eye gene in turn dominates the slant-eye. (See text.)

The distinctive inherited eye shapes of the Mongolians (Chinese, Japanese, Eskimos, etc.) result from fatty under-padding of the lids, and thick folds (*epicanthic*) overlapping the inner corners, giving the eyes almond-shape, or oblique, effects. Mongolian eyes should not be confused with the true 'slant' eyes found among white and other peoples, in which the inner skin folds are absent and the eyes really slant upwards towards the outer corners. Moreover, the genes for the two types of eyes work differently, the genes for Mongolian eyes being dominant, those for true slant eyes recessive. Thus, in matings between a Mongolian and a white, the children will almost always have Mongolian eyes. But if in two white parents one has slant eyes, the other straight eyes, the children are likely to have straight eyes.

Other eye-gene workings include these: In *wide* or *large* eyes, the genes tend to be dominant; if one parent's eyes are wide and/or large, and the other parent's eyes narrow and/or small, their children will tend to have the wide or large eyes. In *deep-set* eyes the genes usually are recessive; if only one parent has such eyes, the child is not likely to have them. The genes for *long eyelashes* are dominant; if one parent has them, they may very well reappear in a child.

With regard to the nose, while one hears it said, 'He has his father's nose', etc., this organ is not inherited as a unit. Its shape and size result from the action of a number of separate genes, governing the sizes and forms of its different parts – the bridge, nostrils, bulb, or tip, and the junction with the upper lip. If a person does have a nose which seems almost a replica of that of one parent, it is likely he received a combination of the nose genes from the parent which dominated those from the other parent. More often a child's nose will resemble that of one parent in only one or two main details, while also showing some characteristics of the other parent's nose. But, in all cases, due allowance should be made for ageing effects and environmental influences on nose shapes. In addition to radical changes in nose shapes at puberty, less perceptible and gradual changes may occur through the years as part of the normal maturing and ageing processes. Often family resemblances in noses become most evident in the older years. On the other hand, hereditary nose characteristics may be masked or cancelled out in individuals by accidents, diseases, plastic operations, effects of abnormal diet or heavy drinking and other environmental factors. All the foregoing facts must be taken into account when tracing inheritance of nose shapes in any family.

As to nose inheritance, if two parents have very different nose shapes – one straight and moderate-sized, the other prominent, hooked, high-bridged, humped or pug-nosed – the genes for the more prominent or extreme details usually dominate, and these tend to reappear in a child. If both parents have rather small, straight, regular noses, the children all are apt to have noses of the same type. However, since the various nose genes may sort out and work independently, one child in a family may have a small nose with large nostrils, another a long nose with small nostrils. Varieties of noses may be found especially in offspring of two mulatto parents who carry both white and Negro nose genes. In matings between whites and Negroes, the children's noses tend to have the high and narrow bridges of the white parents and the broad nostrils of the Negro parents.

Inheritance of *mouth* shapes may be even more complex than of nose shapes. Not only is the mouth much influenced by the structure of the jaws, teeth, palate, and surrounding muscles, but being so movable and in such constant use, its form and appearance are continually and throughout life affected by the person's talking, eating, and sleeping habits, facial expressions and moods. In addition, there are the marked changes in mouth shape that illness and ageing can produce. Hereditary factors in mouth shapes can therefore be identified only after environmental influences are ruled out, and this is not easy. To date conclusions have been arrived at only with respect to the more marked racial differences and a few odd or abnormal conditions.

In mixed matings, the genes for the thick Negro lips tend to dominate. If the Negro parent has no white genes the offspring are all likely to have thick lips. In matings between mulattoes, the offspring may have various types of lips and mouths, showing that a considerable number of different genes are involved.

The '*Hapsburg*' *lip* peculiarity – a protruding lower lip, usually with a narrow, undershot jaw – is named after the royal Spanish and Austrian families in which it has been prevalent for generations. It is dominant in inheritance.

Dimples also are usually hereditary, through a dominant

gene. If this trait is present in one parent, a child has an even chance of being dimpled.

Receding chins tend usually to be recessive to straight; narrow or pointed chins recessive to wide chins. In matings between parents with these different chin shapes, the children are more likely to have straight rather than receding chins, and wide rather than narrow or pointed chins.

In the case of *teeth*, there are marked family tendencies towards various types of teeth and the manner in which upper and lower teeth are set together. But eating habits, diet, tooth care and other conditions may also contribute to these family resemblances. Where direct evidence of inheritance in teeth can best be seen is in the abnormal conditions described in Chapter 13.

Natural differences in *hair form*, from curly to poker-straight, are determined chiefly by the way genes cause the hair to be shaped and to grow out of the hair follicles in the scalp. The genes for the frizziest or curliest types of hair usually dominate those for straighter hair. Most potent is the woolly gene, found largely among Negroes, but sometimes also, though rarely, in whites who have no Negro blood. Next in order of potency, the kinky gene dominates the ordinary curly; the curly dominates the wavy; the wavy dominates the ordinary straight. However, the very thick, straight Mongolian hair is of a special type, and the gene for this may dominate all the others. Thus, in matings between pure Mongolians and whites, and usually between Mongolians and Negroes, the offspring will all have the thick, straight hair. Likewise, in matings between white persons and Negroes with woolly hair, the Negro type of hair will tend to appear in offspring.

Ruling out any artificial changes made in parents' hair, and keeping in mind that hair form may change with age – wavy or curly hair often becoming straighter – here are some predictions of what a child's hair form will be.

Curly hair is rarely likely to appear in a child unless at least one parent has naturally curly hair. If both parents are curly-haired, the chances of the child's being so increase and become almost certain if all of the parents' close relatives are curly-haired. Should there be relatives with wavy hair and/or straight hair, these hair types may also appear in children of curly-haired parents, though with less frequency than curly hair.

Wavy hair in a child results most often if both parents are wavy-haired, or if one parent and all of his or her close relatives are the same. If one parent has wavy hair, the other straight, the chances are even for either type to appear in a

The Hair-Form Genes

One's inherited hair form depends on how genes work to shape the hairs and the follicles out of which they grow

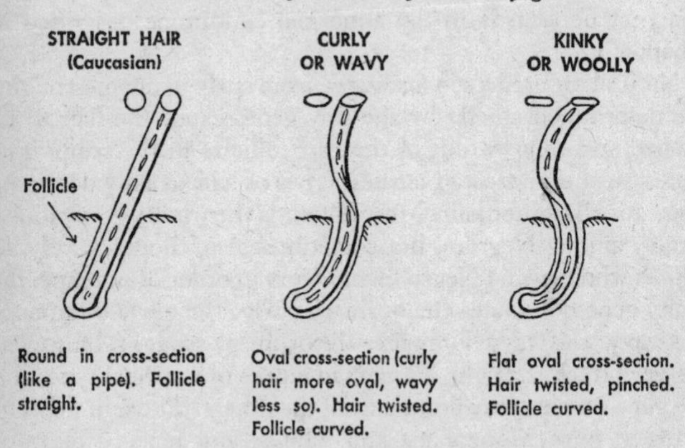

(For inheritance workings, see text.)

child. If both parents are *straight-haired*, their children are almost certain all to have straight hair. If just one parent is *kinky-haired*, and comes from a family with that hair type, the children are all likely to be kinky-haired. But if the one parent has some non-kinky-haired relatives and the other parent has curly, wavy, or straight hair, there is an even chance that the hair of any of their children will not be kinky.

The tendency to have much or little hair on the head or body, or both, is also strongly influenced by heredity. Race differences offer the bext examples. Mongolians (especially full-blooded American Indians) have the least facial and body hair, Negroes have more and whites have the most. The hairiest of all peoples are the primitive Ainus of Japan, who are of white origin.

Heavy eyebrows growing together are most common in Greeks, Turks, Armenians, and other Mediterranean peoples, but also are sometimes found in other groups, including the Irish and Welsh. Apart from the gene workings, hormonal factors may have much to do with the extent of hair growth on the face or body. The most marked differences in this respect are between women and men, with the male sex hormones tending to stimulate such hair growth.

CHAPTER TEN

SHAPE AND STATURE

THE GENERAL SIZES of all human beings, as of animals of other species, are determined by their heredity. The human genes dictate that no person can grow to be as big as an elephant, nor as small as a mouse. Moreover, human stature genes work within a much narrower range than do those of many other species: for example, there are no such size differences among human beings as among dogs – a giant Saint Bernard or a pint-sized Mexican Chihuahua. It is because the differences in human stature are so limited that we often attach such importance to a few inches more or less in height. At the same time, the limited differences have made it difficult to study stature inheritance, with added complications resulting from the fact that the influences of environment on stature must always be taken into account.

In terms of groups, the very tallest human beings today are African Negroes of the Lake Chad tribes, near the lower Nile, whose males average 6 feet 1 inch in height, with many 7 feet and over. The smallest humans are the pygmy Negrillos, also of Africa, whose adult males average 4 feet 6 inches. (Midgets and giants are in the abnormal category. See Chapter 13.) Apart from these extremes the differences between peoples of stocks we call tall, such as the Swedes, and those we call short, such as the Japanese or Italians, may be a matter of only two or three inches on the average. The principal reasons why the stature differences of the various human ethnic stocks are not greater is that there has been constant interbreeding among them, and that no attempt was ever made to breed human groups deliberately for tallness or shortness.

In any group, and under any conditions, a major factor in determining height is an individual's *sex*. Given exactly the same stature genes, a male will grow about 6 per cent taller than a female, or somewhat over three quarters of an inch more to each foot of her size. Thus, among Americans at this writing, men average just above 5 feet 8 inches (174 cm.),* women 5 feet 4 inches (164 cm.). This difference can be little more attributed to environmental factors, such as work activities, diet, living habits, etc., than can the differences in size between bulls and cows, or roosters and hens. Obviously, the internal chemical differences between the sexes, set in motion by their respective XX and XY chromosome mechanisms, cause their skeletal and bodily developments to diverge not only in size, but in proportions. But this indicates that in individuals of either sex, special internal chemical factors may also modify the activity of their stature genes and the development of their bodily details. Some of these factors may be hereditary, some environmental, and some a combination of the two.

Just as plants and flowers grow taller if they are in good soil and are properly watered and tended, or can be stunted if conditions are poor, so the statures of human beings also can be considerably influenced by their environments. Although human genes have changed little in thousands of years, people of modern times are considerably taller than were those of ancient and medieval periods. Most noticeable have been the changes in the past half century, with the new generations of Americans being taller than their grandparents by an average of about two inches. Especially marked increases are among offspring of various immigrant stocks, with frequent cases of sons four to six inches taller than their fathers. In most European countries, and in many other advanced countries, including Japan, increases in stature have also been noted. For the most part this increase has been attributed to great improvements in diet, living conditions, and medical care. However, some scientists believe that changes in the earth's climate, and in meteorological and cosmic conditions, have added to the stature increase.

How much taller can people grow? Many experts think that in about two hundred years more the average height of

* In Britain, men average 5 feet 9 inches, women 5 feet 3 inches.

American males will be at least six feet, with a great many up to seven feet or somewhat over, while the average American woman will be about as tall as the average man now is. Any much greater height may bring difficulties. As will be noted in Chapter 13, giants of eight feet or over have tended to be weak, glandular cases, usually short-lived.

Whatever the environmental conditions may be anywhere, it is evident that tendencies towards greater height run in some families, and towards lesser height in others. How the stature genes work is not precisely known, but as a rule it appears that the shortness genes dominate the tallness genes. This means that a tall person probably is not carrying any shortness genes, and that if two tall persons mate, all their children will be tall, except in individual cases where diseases, dietary deficiencies, hormonal upsets, etc., may stunt normal growth. Short persons may or may not be carrying hidden tallness genes; they probably are not if they are of short stocks on both sides and if this shortness was not due to environmental factors. But if they had or have some close relatives who are tall, they may very well be carrying hidden genes for tallness, and may produce children much taller than themselves. This is especially likely to be so with persons who had grown up under unfavourable conditions, as with those of various immigrant groups. (See preceding sections.) Where one parent is genetically short, and the other tall, the odds are somewhat greater that the children will be short rather than tall.

In judging inheritance of stature, or drawing conclusions with respect to individuals, full allowance should be made for age changes that have taken place or may take place, and for the fact that different individuals have different growth rates, even with the same stature genes. Males sometimes do not reach their full height until age twenty-three, females not until twenty-one. Some shrinkage in height in men and women may begin to occur as early as age thirty, becoming more pronounced with added years, so that by age seventy, a man may be about one inch or more shorter than he was at twenty-five.

While skeletal structure is largely determined by heredity,

as is stature, a person's 'upholstery' – the muscles, fat, and tissues – can be most strongly influenced by environment. Thus, where an individual's height remains almost the same from maturity on (except for the slight decline with ageing, just noted), the outer body form may change frequently, and sometimes radically within a short time. Moreover, occupations and living habits can do much to influence the structure and outer form of the body or its parts, as is shown in certain bodily characteristics common to farmers, sailors, dancers, etc. Such environmental characteristics may be mistaken for inherited traits when they appear in successive members of families who have worked at the same tasks for generations. Nevertheless, with full allowance for the environmental influences, definite tendencies towards given proportions and details of the body are strongly conditioned by a person's genetic make-up.

Obesity, in particular, has received much attention in the current period when so many people are weight-conscious. Although many complex factors, both physical and psychological, are generally involved in obesity, there is evidence that tendencies towards fatness or slenderness may have an hereditary basis. In lower animals some strains of a species have been bred which are excessively fat, others lean. Also, in human beings, studies of twins show that obesity is far more often a common trait of both members of an identical pair than of a fraternal pair, or of non-twin siblings.

Obesity genes, it is believed, affect the body's metabolism, causing certain individuals to put on much more fat per pound of food consumed than do others, or increasing the proportion of weight gain that is fatty tissue. This does not mean that even metabolic obesity is always, or most often, due to heredity, since many of these cases are traceable to acquired diseases. Further, when all members of a family are fat it may often be because of their similar diets and ways of living. But when environmental causes are minimal, genetic studies indicate that a predisposition towards obesity may be produced by dominant genes, with tendencies towards leanness produced by recessive genes. Thus, on this basis, slender parents, carrying no obesity genes, will usually have only slender children. But fat parents, while tending to have fat children, may be carrying hidden slimness genes, and so may also have some slender children.

Whatever the special effects of body-form genes may be, a most important fact is that their general workings are very different in males and females. Just as the same stature genes produce greater height in the male than the female, the same body-form genes, as in a brother and sister, have divergent effects on almost every detail of their skeletal structure and fleshy parts. In the male, the bones are relatively thicker and heavier, as are the muscles; the chest is larger and broader; the hands and feet are longer, blunter, and heavier. (Skull differences between males and females, as affecting their features, were described in the preceding chapter.) In the female, the shoulders are relatively narrower and more sloping and the hips are wider and bigger, because the hip structure is both broader than in the males, and covered with more fat. The extra fatty layers found in females, as a rule, in addition to their softer muscles, contribute towards making their contours more rounded than those of the male. A seldom-noted sex difference is in the alignment of the arm and leg bones: in the male the upper and lower arms are usually in line when the arm is held straightened out against the side, whereas in the female the lower arm tends to jut out from the elbow. (See illustration, page 80.) Also, females tend to be more knock-kneed, in part because their hips are wider and their thighs heavier.

Different sizes and shapes of *breasts* in women may result from different types of breast genes, although diet, health factors, physical activities, and childbearing and nursing are modifying influences. Some of the most striking hereditary breast types are found in women of certain African tribes. The genes for any type of female breasts, it should be noted, can be transmitted as easily through the father as through the mother. This explains why, in many cases, a mother may note that a grown daughter has distinctive breasts not like hers, but like those of the husband's mother or one of his sisters. (A son, similarly, can inherit, through his mother, male bodily traits that are like those of her male relatives rather than his father's.)

Much of the work of the sex genes in shaping bodily details in either male or female directions is carried out through the way they construct and influence the sex glands – the testes in the male, ovaries in the female. This is shown by what happens if these glands are removed, or if the production of their normal quotas of male and female hormones is radically changed. If a male is castrated before he achieves puberty, his body will develop many of the feminine characteristics (wider hips, soft muscles, lack of facial hair, etc.). If the sex glands in a young woman do not function properly before or during puberty (or if they are removed through operation as is sometimes necessary), her breasts, hips, and contours may not develop in the normal female way. Often in these cases a girl may also grow unusually tall. (Proper medical treatment given in time, with the supplement of the required sex hormones, may help to prevent or correct these deviations from normal body development.) However, if the glandular changes or upsets occur *after* puberty, when the skeletal structure is wet, the effects on the outward sex characteristics are much less. Castration of an adult male will in time make him flabbier and fattier in his tissues, but in a woman, removal of the ovaries after maturity usually has very little outward effect.

Head shape – whether a person is roundheaded (*brachycephalic*) or longheaded (*dolichocephalic*) in maturity – depends largely on heredity, but diet and living conditions are modifying influences. While all shapes of heads are found among all peoples, round heads (broad oval) predominate among the Mongolians, long heads (long oval) among Negroes. Among whites one head shape may be more prevalent in some groups, another head shape in other groups. As a rule, if parents have different head shapes, the roundhead genes tend to dominate those for long heads. But any predictions of head-shape inheritance should take into consideration environmental influences.

For instance, stature has a relationship to head shape, since a lengthening of the body bones may also bring a lengthening of the skull. Thus, the increase in stature in the United States has brought some lengthening of heads, and particularly in immigrant stocks, offspring may have head shapes somewhat different from their parents.

Sex Characteristics in Limbs

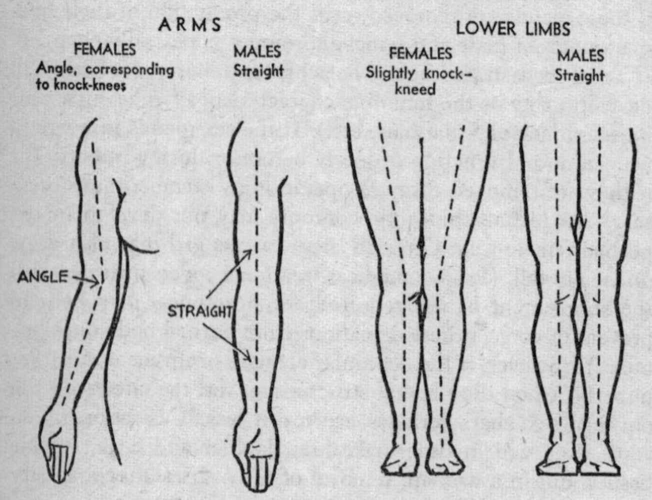

(From *The New* YOU AND HEREDITY. Copyright 1939, 1950 by Amram Scheinfeld.)

Inherited factors in shapes of hands, feet, chests, muscles, etc., have been studied mainly with respect to abnormal traits, to be discussed in Chapter 13.

CHAPTER ELEVEN

THE 'BAD' GENES

ALTHOUGH IMPROVEMENTS IN environment and medical science have made human beings healthier and sounder in body than ever before in the world's history, there unfortunately are a great many inborn defects that continue to assert themselves. Some of these affect outward appearances; others affect some inner organ or process. Of greatest concern are the inherited defects or abnormalities that severely handicap the person, or doom him to suffering, or cause premature death. Fortunately, most of the serious ills and defects directly and chiefly produced by heredity are not too prevalent, many of those in which heredity plays an indirect part may often be prevented by early safeguards; and even hereditary ailments that already have asserted themselves may in many cases be eased or cured by prompt and effective treatment. (It is a common mistake to assume that because a condition is hereditary nothing can be done about it.)

Another fact on the optimistic side is that many human afflictions which in the past were blamed on bad heredity have now been proved to be mainly or entirely due to bad environment. In every case, then, when individuals or members of a family are concerned about a given disease or defect which they know, believe, or suspect is hereditary, it is important that they have the basic facts. These facts, with respect to all except very rare conditions of limited interest, we shall try to present in this and succeeding chapters. (See Index for any given condition.)

When is a defect 'hereditary'? There is much confusion on this point. For instance, even doctors sometimes wrongly use the terms *congenital*, *familial*, and *hereditary* as if they meant the same thing. But this may or may not always be so. Here are the differences:

Congenital refers to a condition present at birth. This need not mean that it is hereditary. While heredity is responsible for or involved in many congenital abnormalities, perhaps the majority are purely environmental. That is, they are *acquired* by the developing baby at some stage before birth, through various unfortunate factors in the mother's womb, such as improper nourishment, lack of certain needed substances, hormonal upsets, or prenatal accidents. Also, if there are disease germs in the mother, these may affect the baby and cause it to be born with a congenital disease. *Congenital syphilis* is one example of a disease that can be present at birth and not be hereditary. Although it was long thought that syphilis could be inherited (the theme of Ibsen's famous drama *Ghosts*), we know now that neither this nor any other germ disease can be passed along through a parent's genes or chromosomes. The only way any germ disease can appear in a newborn baby is through infection from the mother. (Sometimes a mother can carry the syphilis germs received from the father, without having contracted the disease herself.) *Tuberculosis* is another disease that can appear in a newborn baby through infection by the mother.

Familial is a term whose meaning, as applied to various conditions, is frequently misunderstood. The mere fact that a disease or defect is repeated in parents and children, or has run in a family for several generations, is again no proof that it is hereditary. Very often the condition is due solely to such environmental factors as dietary deficiencies, bad living or working habits, lack of hygiene or proper medical care, infections, diseases, or other harmful influences. It may be only these same influences running in a family that produce the same given diseases or defects. If the environments are changed, such familial conditions will disappear. But again, as with congenital diseases, a great many familial conditions *are* hereditary, wholly or in some degree.

Hereditary is a term that can be applied to a condition *only if it is produced by a defective gene or genes carried in the chromosomes* received from the father and/or mother. Defective genes may work in a wide variety of ways, and at different stages of life. Some hereditary conditions are also congenital, but a great many others are not, since they may not appear until late in childhood, or maturity, or old age. Similarly, hereditary conditions are familial only when the genes producing them are fairly simple and direct in their workings, causing a given condition to reappear in members of a family for successive generations. However, hereditary conditions are often *not* familial. This may be true of rare recessive conditions, the two required genes for which may be brought together by a husband and wife in neither of whose families the disease or defect had previously appeared. In other conditions complex gene-workings, and perhaps special environmental factors as well, may keep a hereditary condition from cropping up except in occasional instances. And sometimes a defective gene may have suddenly arisen through a change (mutation), in the mother's egg or father's sperm, so that there would have been no family history of the condition. (See Chapters 3, 25, pages 32 and 212.)

The great importance of distinguishing between *non-hereditary* and *hereditary* conditions lies in this fact: if a condition is non-hereditary, it offers no threat at all to the children or relatives of an afflicted person, unless it is a contagious disease, and even then only if transmitted by direct personal contact, but once such a disease is cured, all threats to others cease. But if a condition is hereditary, the threat of transmission is always there, no matter whether the person carrying the genes for it is himself afflicted, or was afflicted and had been cured. In short, all non-hereditary conditions could be wiped out completely and quickly by changing the conditions causing them. But hereditary conditions will continue as long as the genes producing them are passed along.

How do 'bad' genes work? In many ways they are like individuals who misbehave, or don't do their jobs properly, or create serious difficulties for others. Some 'bad' genes may be recklessly overactive, producing too many fingers or toes, or too much of some chemical in the body. Other genes may be shiftless and underactive, not completing the job to which they are assigned and leaving serious flaws in some vital part of the body or its functioning. (Where these genetic flaws apply specifically to one or another of the body's chemical processes, they are called 'inborn errors of metabolism'.) Still other genes work properly only up to a certain stage of life, and then become shiftless, irresponsible, or worse. Again, many 'bad' genes produce only a single, distinctive defect, without impairing anything else in the body's workings. But other 'bad' genes, if they are in a key position, particularly at the beginning of life, may start off a chain of defective processes, creating many defects. Such multiple defects that arise from the workings of a single gene are called *syndromes*. Finally, as with human workers, some 'bad' genes go wrong only if in the company of certain other genes, or only in certain environments. (Examples of all these types of genes will be found among the specific conditions to be discussed in the following chapters. See also illustration, page 25.)

Some persons, because of defective genes, have a special weakness in one part of the body or another – brain, heart, lungs, digestive system, or nervous system. Under average or favourable conditions, these persons may function normally. But if there is some unusual stress, or some adverse factor in the environment (infections, dietary deficiencies, etc.) they may have breakdowns or develop diseases, whereas individuals without the defective genes would escape these ills. In all such cases persons are spoken of as having inherited 'predispositions', 'tendencies' or 'susceptibilities' to given diseases. As will be noted in later chapters, many mental disorders, heart afflictions, and other serious ailments may depend for their development on degrees of such inherited predispositions.

The force with which a gene works under given circumstances is an important factor in determining whether a condition will assert itself. *Penetrance* is the term geneticists use to describe the strength of a gene. If it manifests its effects under all circumstances, it is said to have '100 per cent penetrance'; if only in half the cases, '50 per cent penetrance', etc. Thus, a condition caused by a single dominant gene with 100 per cent penetrance may appear without a break in generation after generation of a family. But should a gene be incompletely dominant, with partial penetrance (75 per cent, 50 per cent, 40 per cent or whatever), its effects may be discontinuous, failing to show through in many individuals who inherit it.

Also, just as many 'dominant' genes are not always completely dominant, many, if not most genes for recessive diseases may produce some mild effects even in the single state, when coupled with a dominant gene. The importance of this fact will be discussed in a later section. (See page 89.)

In extremely rare instances two normal parents may unexpectedly produce a child with a defect that is always known to be caused by a single gene (either a simple dominant, or, in sons only, a sex-linked recessive). When it is clear that neither parent could have inherited the gene from his or her family, it may be assumed that the child's defective gene had arisen through a new mutation in a germ cell of one of the parents. Geneticists now estimate roughly that on the average any given gene mutates about once in 30,000 to 50,000 times; also, that some genes are more unstable than others, and mutate considerably oftener than this average, while some very stable genes mutate much less frequently.

There are many important differences in the ways in which hereditary diseases and defects afflict males as compared with females – *usually to the disadvantage of the male.* In some conditions the hereditary action is direct, as when it involves genes in the sex chromosomes. In other conditions there are general inborn sex differences, in the body construction, body chemistry, organs, and functions, which produce differences in the susceptibility or resistance of males and females to given diseases. In still other conditions the environments of males and females (their jobs, activities, or habits) may be mainly responsible for the different ways or degrees in which they are afflicted; but even here one must not forget that inborn sex factors may have much to do with directing lives of males and females into different environmental channels.

Altogether, it is now recognized that in almost every important disease – mental, organic, functional, infectious – the sex of the individual plays a role in its development and severity. And most amazing, it is becoming increasingly clear that *males, not females, are the weaker sex* biologically. For, as a group, males are more often born defective, are more likely to suffer from heredity ailments, are inherently more susceptible to most major diseases, and when afflicted are more likely to succumb. Females are inherently at a disadvantage in only a few categories – afflictions linked with child-bearing and their sex organs, cancers restricted to their sex, gallstones, and diabetes, goitre, and certain other glandular diseases.

The fact that inborn, and not environmental, factors are mainly responsible for the greater biological weakness of males is clearly shown by the situation before birth. Among unborn babies the males who die off are markedly more numerous than the females, ranging from perhaps twice as many in the first months after conception to about 30 per cent more in the later months. Among defective and abnormal babies, miscarried or born, the proportion of males is again very much higher. And in infancy and early childhood – before environments or conditioning differ – males continue to die off, become diseased, or develop defects, at a higher rate than females. The same is true among many lower animals, from insects to higher mammals. There seems little doubt, then, that females are endowed with many genetic advantages over males.

The reason the inborn advantages of human females were not so apparent in the past was that they were so often cancelled out by the strains and mortality tolls of unlimited childbearing. Another reason was (and still is in many backward countries) that very poor environments give the minor inherent female advantages much less chance to assert themselves. But today, as environments have steadily improved, and the special hazards of women have been greatly reduced – much more so than have the special hazards of men – all of women's biological advantages are being manifested to an increasing extent. (See also Chapter 18.)

Among the hereditary conditions that most clearly discriminate against males are those called *sex-linked*, in which the genes

Sex-Linked Inheritance

If a defective gene is in the 'X' chromosome (as in color blindness)—

FEMALE (Carrier) X X

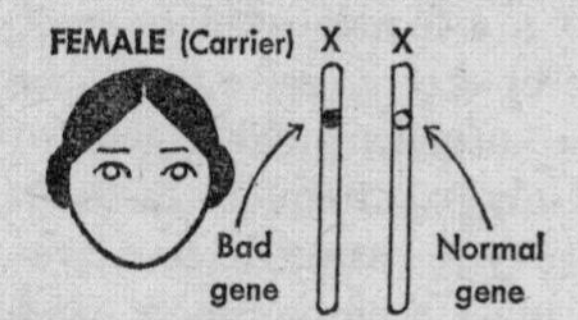

With two X's, a female carrier usually has a normal X gene to block the bad one, and is herself normal.

X **MALE** (Afflicted)

Bad gene →

Y

With only one X, male has no normal gene to block the bad one and develops the defect.

WOMAN CARRIER'S SONS

One in two gets mother's bad 'X gene and has the defect.

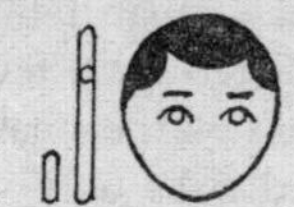

One in two gets mother's normal 'X" and is not defective.

AFFLICTED MAN'S SONS

Normal X ← gene from mother

← Father's ' Y

No son gets father's X, so every son is free of the defect and cannot pass on the bad gene.

WOMAN CARRIER'S DAUGHTERS

One in two gets mother's bad X, and is a carrier like mother.

One in two gets the normal X, and cannot pass on defect.

AFFLICTED MAN'S DAUGHTERS

Every daughter gets the father's bad X and is a carrier (like woman at top left of page).

AFFLICTED FEMALE

Only when a female gets an X with a bad gene from both parents will she develop the defect.

Every one of her sons will have this same defect. Every daughter will be a carrier of the gene.

responsible are in the sex chromosomes – chiefly the large X. Since females carry two X's, but no Y, and males carry only one X, coupled with a Y, defective sex-linked genes work differently in the two sexes, with the males much more often affected. The reason is mainly that if a female receives an X chromosome with a defective gene of the recessive type, her other X chromosome usually has a normal matching gene to block the effects of the bad gene. Only in infrequent cases do both X chromosomes of a female carry the same defective recessive gene. However, if a male's single X chromosome has a bad gene, this gene alone usually produces a defect in him, for it is highly unlikely that his small Y chromosome would carry a matching normal gene. Thus, a great many conditions, of which the best known are *colour blindness* and *haemophilia*, are inherited far more often by males than females. In addition, males, exclusively, may be afflicted by a few rare conditions believed to be produced by genes on the small Y chromosome. As for females, they run added risks only in the limited instances where defective genes in the X chromosome are dominant.

In all conditions where the defective gene is in the X chromosome, transmission to a male can obviously be only through his mother, from whom he receives his single X. Thus, if one of the mother's X's is defective and one normal, the son has an even chance either of inheriting the given defect or escaping it. Should both the mother's X's carry the same defective recessive gene (which means that she herself would show the affliction) no son could escape inheriting the defect. An afflicted male, in turn, cannot transmit a recessive X-gene condition to his son, who receives only his father's Y chromosome. As for a daughter, while she is certain to get any defective gene carried in the single X chromosome she receives from her father, it will usually cause no damage unless she receives a matching X-chromosome gene from her mother. In the great majority of cases, therefore, sex-linked recessive defects skip a generation, passing from affected fathers through unaffected daughters to affected grandsons.

Only a small number of defective genes in the X chromosome are of the dominant type. In these cases, an afflicted father will transmit the genes and the resulting condition to *each of his daughters*, but to none of his sons. If a mother is afflicted, there is the same fifty-fifty risk for her sons and daughters alike.

Doctors are now recognizing that knowledge of hereditary diseases or defects in a patient, or in members of his or her family, may prove important in various ways. This is why they ask details about family histories. Often the information is highly useful in diagnosing early symptoms and taking preventive measures. Where a hereditary condition has already made serious progress in a patient, examination of close blood relatives, particularly younger ones, may often reveal similar hereditary threats, which can be staved off through prompt treatment. Apart from this, the facts about disease inheritance may have great importance to parents or prospective parents who know, or suspect, they carry genes for one condition or another, and can weigh the dangers to their children.

What may prove to be among the most important findings of medical genetics is that persons who are themselves not afflicted (or not yet afflicted) by various hereditary diseases, but are carrying genes for them, may be identified by certain special characteristics in their blood, or eyes, or body chemistry, etc. This applies particularly to individuals carrying a single gene for conditions whose serious effects are produced by a pair of the genes. The most striking examples to date are the carriers of single genes for either *sickle-cell anaemia* or *Mediterranean anaemia*, who show easily detectable symptoms in their blood. Also, there is limited evidence that tests may identify unafflicted carriers of genes for diabetes, pernicious anaemia, schizophrenia, epilepsy and other diseases, and women carriers of single genes for colour blindness, haemophilia and other sex-linked conditions. Tests are also being developed to identify younger adults who carry genes for and may ultimately develop Huntington's chorea, hereditary ataxia and several other conditions with late onset. There is hope of eventually greatly extending the identification both of the now unknown carriers of defective genes, and of persons who themselves have inherited a susceptibility to given diseases.

But in the case of any given hereditary condition, an absolute essential is that the doctor and the afflicted person (or one who fears transmitting the gene for the condition) should know the precise mechanism of its inheritance wherever established. Thus, throughout our disease and defect chapters, the known or suspected gene-workings of all important conditions will be given: whether dominant, recessive, or sex-linked. General information about how the different types of genes work and detailed facts about the sex-linked genes have already been presented. Here we will summarize and stress the essential details about the dominant and recessive diseases and defects.

A *dominant* condition is one in which a single gene, passed on by one parent, can produce the given defect. Where the gene is a *simple dominant*, the gene almost always shows its effects. And if a parent has such a condition, there is a fifty-fifty chance any child will also be afflicted. If both parents have the condition, there is a three-in-four threat to any child. However, some dominant genes are *qualified*, or *incomplete*, in their workings, depending for their expression on the presence of other genes, or on adverse factors in the environment. Where this applies to a gene, an afflicted parent may transmit the gene to a child without the latter in many cases developing the parent's condition, or one child with the gene may develop the defect, another with the same gene may not, or may have the condition in a milder or somewhat different form.

A *recessive* condition is one in which at least *two* of the same genes, one from each parent, are needed to produce the given defect or disease. Where the genes are *simple recessives*, if both parents are afflicted with the condition, every child will be. If neither parent is afflicted, but each is carrying a hidden gene for the condition, there is a one-in-four chance the child will develop it. If only one parent is afflicted, and the other does not carry the gene for the condition, no child will develop the affliction. (Examples are common diabetes and albinism.) But as with dominant genes, some recessives are qualified in their action, showing their effects only under certain adverse conditions or when coupled with other genes. In these qualified cases, even if both parents have the defect or disease in question, a child with the genes may often escape developing the condition.

In weighing the hereditary threats for any specific condition, the non-medical reader should be cautioned not to draw precise conclusions without having had competent medical opinion beforehand, so that he will be sure the condition is the one referred to in the text and is inherited in the way stated. In many cases the same or similar conditions can be produced either by heredity or by environmental factors (as with various types of deafness, blindness, muscular ailments, etc.). The doctor himself should study the family history, and if necessary, check medical literature and/or consult with a medical geneticist, to make sure the condition in question is or is not of the hereditary type.

The *time of onset* is also important in many conditions that appear at different stages of life: at birth, in childhood or maturity, or not until middle age or old age. (Examples are cataracts and chronic simple glaucoma.) Where the same condition appears in some families only at one stage of life, in other families at another stage, different genes working in different ways may be involved. Thus, in checking on some variable-onset condition, not only the precise nature of the condition, but the approximate age of the afflicted members of a family, must be known.

CHAPTER TWELVE

INHERITANCE IN MAJOR ORGANIC DISEASES

TOPPING THE LIST of major diseases are the heart and blood-vessel disorders. These now account for more than half of the deaths in the United States annually.* Chief killers among them are high blood pressure (*hypertension*); hardening and thickening of the arteries (*arteriosclerosis*); and rheumatic heart disease (or rheumatic fever). Medical authorities believe that hereditary factors are involved in all these conditions by way of some degree of predisposition. This means that where any one of these conditions runs in a family, an individual member may have an above-average risk of developing it. The threat is considerably greater as a rule for males, whose death rate from heart and arterial diseases is much higher than that of females. The difference is no longer believed entirely due to the greater strain under which men live and work, or to other conditions to which they are exposed. Various studies indicate that inborn male weaknesses are also involved. (See Chapter 11, page 85).

Hypertension (high blood pressure) may result from other diseases, or may also lead to other diseases, such as enlarged heart and heart failure, coronary artery disease with blood clots, kidney disease, apoplectic stroke or brain haemorrhage. It is very probable that a predisposition to hypertension is hereditary, although environmental factors are also very important in bringing it on. Some authorities claim a single dominant gene may cause susceptibility to the condition in some families, but that has not yet been proved. In any event, where there is a history of hypertension in one's family, a medical check-up is urged to reveal possible threats.

Arteriosclerosis involves thickening and hardening of the

* In Britain, deaths from these causes average 46 per cent.

arteries, with impairment of blood circulation, leading to heart pains (*angina pectoris*) or damage to the heart muscle (*coronary thrombosis*) and strokes or brain damage. There is no clear evidence of its heredity, but suspicion of it is greatest in cases of *atherosclerosis*, where there are fatty deposits in the arteries caused by improper metabolism of the body's fatty substances. Arteriosclerosis is common in persons with gout, which may be hereditary.

In *varicose veins*, the principal causes and factors are probably in most cases environmental, the condition being commonest among persons whose work requires continued standing, and among women after childbirth. In some families, however, a tendency to varicose veins may be inherited, perhaps through an irregularly dominant gene. In such cases if a parent has the condition, the chance is still less than even for any child to be afflicted with it.

Rheumatic fever (or childhood rheumatism), which afflicts about one in fifty children, may possibly run in families by way of a *susceptibility*, perhaps genetically determined. The disease apparently develops only under certain conditions still not clearly identified, although it is believed that if the tendency is there, the condition will result from repeated streptococcal infections of the nose and throat. Poor diet and bad, overcrowded living conditions seem to increase the chance of this disease's appearing; nevertheless, it also on occasion strikes children in the most favoured groups. Wherever rheumatic fever has previously appeared in a family, it is urgently advised that all younger members be examined for possible symptoms. Prompt antibiotic treatments may overcome the worst threats.

In *congenital heart disease*, a number of types resulting from malformations of the heart or blood vessels involved in its functions may be hereditary. Remedial operations are possible in many of these cases.

Cancer remains one of the most baffling of all human afflictions. There is no proof as yet that heredity is directly responsible for any of the common cancers, although some rare forms of cancer are definitely inherited. Many authorities believe, however, that different individuals are born with varied degrees of susceptibility to given types of common cancer, and that such degrees of susceptibility or predisposition do run in families. The evidence to date shows only that: (1) The incidence of cancer of the breast, or lungs, or uterus, or other parts of the body, is considerably above average in some families, and where a particular type of cancer has appeared previously in a person's close relatives, he or she has a greater-than-average risk of developing the same condition. (2) Among identical twins, if one has cancer, the other is much more likely to develop cancer of the same type, and sooner, than is the case with fraternal twins. (3) 'Cancer-susceptible' strains have been found in lower animals, and it has been possible to breed strains of mice and other experimental animals that will develop given types of cancer according to regular rules of inheritance. However, it has also been shown that cancers can be produced artificially by radiation, chemicals, and hundreds of different irritants; that the cancer incidence in human beings is greatly affected by various conditions that are in no wise hereditary; and that even if there are hereditary predispositions, cancer can often be prevented from developing, or if it develops can be cured in a growing proportion of cases.

Cancer is known to develop when a group of cells in any part of the body 'go haywire', or begin to behave abnormally, producing malignant growths. As these cancerous cells multiply, they starve out and destroy surrounding tissues and vital organs, and then may break loose and range like outlaws through the blood stream, creating general havoc. In this process heredity may play a part, theoretically, by way of certain defective genes which could work to (1) derange the cell activities at a given stage of life, particularly during the older ages when body tissues weaken; (2) produce unusual chemical substances or hormones that might irritate cells into becoming cancerous; (3) construct some cells so improperly that it would be easy for cancer to develop under various irritating influences; (4) make the cells unusually susceptible to certain viruses or other cancer-producing agencies. Through any of these theoretical situations, particular combinations of defective genes in given families could cause particular types of cancer to appear with much more than average frequency. But the reader is cautioned not to draw conclusions about hereditary cancer threats in his own case until his doctor has confirmed the facts. For one thing, different types of cancer need not be related. Moreover, the same type of cancer may run in a family only because the members for successive generations were exposed to the same cancer-inducing influences, as in the case of miners, quarry workers, pottery makers, etc., who are in constant contact with irritating dust and substances.

Highly important in cancer are the differences in the incidence and nature of cancers in the two sexes, which arise mainly from differences in the sex organs and breasts. But differences in the body's functioning, work, and external environments also are involved. Females naturally run the special risk of developing cancers of the womb, cervix, ovaries, and breasts, while males have a considerable special cancer risk associated with their prostate glands and testes. On the other hand, in the non-sexual cancers of the skin, lips, mouth, tongue, throat, lungs, stomach, etc., the male death rate is very much higher. Whether this is entirely due to the greater exposure of males to cancer-inducing conditions and irritants is doubtful. Recent findings are that hormones play a part in the development, and also the treatment of cancer, which suggests that the important hormonal differences between males and females, arising to begin with through the sex chromosomes, may also be involved in the different ways cancers occur and progess in the two sexes.

In *breast cancer*, despite conflicting reports and theories, there is enough suspicion of hereditary influence so that if several women in a family have been or are afflicted by it, the daughters or sisters should have periodic examinations in their mature years, and prompt treatment if there are any questionable symptoms. However, the appearance of breast cancer in several successive generations – grandmother, mother, daughter – need not of itself prove inheritance, first because the condition is so common that it might be merely coincidence; second, because the breast cancers in different members might be of different and unrelated types, which had started out at different locations.

In *intestinal cancer* heredity may play a considerable part. The strongest evidence is in the case of *multiple polyps of the colon* (smooth growths), which occur in early adult life and in some families are inherited through a dominant gene. Despite doubt on this point, it is urgently advised that whenever one person in a family has developed intestinal cancer, the younger members should be immediately examined for possible symptoms.

In *stomach cancer* heredity may possibly be a factor, since the risk of developing stomach cancer for children or siblings of an afflicted person is more than twice the general average. But unfavourable diet may help to bring on the condition.

Prostate cancer has been reported in some studies as being influenced by heredity, with the condition having a much more than average incidence among relatives of men afflicted with it. In women, *cancer of the uterus* does not appear to be more than slightly influenced by heredity, if at all.

Lung cancer as yet offers no evidence of any hereditary predisposition, but the environmental influence is clearly shown by the marked increase in lung cancer in recent decades. Whether this has been due to more cigarette smoking, as some authorities claim, or mainly to other recent irritating influences (such as industrial smoke and dust), is still being debated.

Skin cancers, of the common types, are very largely due to environmental factors of various kinds. However, a person's inherited skin pigmentation may have something to do with the chances of developing skin or lip cancer under exposure to the sun. Thus, fair-skinned persons run a higher chance of developing skin cancer in the tropics than do the dark-skinned natives. Where skin cancer inheritance does clearly occur is in the case of a number of very rare conditions (not to be confused with common skin cancers). These include *malignant freckles* (*xeroderma pigmentosum*); *epiloia* ('butterfly rash'); and *neurofibromatosis* (coffee-coloured spots).

In *leukaemia*, a blood-cell cancer, one of the types (chronic myeloid), may arise through a chromosome abnormality. However, many cases of leukaemia may be due to environmental factors, among them radiation in repeated or heavy doses.

Diabetes (the 'sugar sickness') is in most cases mainly the result of a predisposition inherited through recessive genes. This means that the inheritance must come through *both* parents, one gene from each. (Some geneticists claim that in certain instances the disease can be produced by a dominant gene, passed on by only one parent, but this remains doubtful.) The actual cause of the disease is failure of the pancreas to secrete enough insulin to convert the sugar in the body processes properly, leading to excess sugar in the system, which may have serious results unless preventive measures are taken. Unfavourable fatty diets, obesity, overeating, nervous strains, infections, and the effects of certain other diseases may serve to bring on diabetes or worsen it; but there is no definite evidence that the disease will develop without some inherited tendency. Especially significant is the fact that many hundreds of children each year in the United States develop diabetes, usually despite good diets and wholesome conditions, leading to the conclusion that they are victims of diabetic heredity.

Additional evidence for the inheritance of a diabetic tendency is provided by these facts: (1) One in four diabetics has diabetic relatives, a far higher than average incidence. (2) Twin studies show that in identical twins, if one has diabetes, so has the other in almost every case. (3) Diabetes has been shown to be inherited in some strains of mice, independently of any environmental influences. Also of interest is the fact that diabetes is one of the few major diseases that afflicts more women than men. The reasons for this are women's generally greater susceptibility to glandular diseases; the effects of childbearing; and the longer life span of women, bringing more of them into the 'diabetic' ages.

In *goitre* the possible part played by heredity is uncertain because development of the common, simple form of goitre depends largely on lack of sufficient iodine in the food or drinking water, causing a strain on and swelling of the thyroid gland. However, even under the same conditions there is evidence that members of some families are much more likely than others to develop goitre, leading to the belief that weakness in the thyroid gland may be inherited (possibly through recessive genes). Should there be any susceptibility, the females in a family run about four times as great a risk of developing goitre as do the males, since the female system apparently needs more iodine. A special danger is that when a mother has a thyroid deficiency there is an increased chance of her giving birth to a *cretin* (a type of mental defective). In any family where goitre has appeared, a first precaution is to see that there is always enough iodine in the diet. *Exophthalmic goitre* (*Graves' disease*) is similar to common goitre in a number of ways but may be more serious and most often afflicts young women who are highly nervous and slender. As in common goitre, inheritance has not been established.

Ulcers (of the stomach and intestines) are now considered to be principally brought on by nervous strain, but some authorities believe there is a possibility also of inherited predispositions. For one thing, stomach ulcers are being found in some babies. Further, the very much higher incidence and seriousness of stomach ulcers in men than in women may be linked in some degree with inherent differences in glandular secretions.

Kidney disease in its most common form, *nephritis*, which is one of the top causes of death, gives no clear evidence of being directly influenced by heredity. However, a rare type, *polycystic disease* of the kidneys (especially serious to pregnant women), appears to be inherited in some cases through a dominant gene.

Fibrosis of the pancreas is another serious organic disease that can be inherited, usually through recessive genes. It afflicts perhaps one in eight hundred white children, most often fatally, but is much rarer in Negroes, and is almost never found in persons of Mongolian stock.

Tuberculosis is basically an environmental, germ-caused disease. The only possible role that heredity can play in this disease is perhaps to make some persons more susceptible to the tuberculosis germs, and others more resistant. Studies among twins in families where tuberculosis has appeared, and with experimental animals, indicate that the chances of developing or resisting tuberculosis, may be influenced by inheritance. However, any inherited 'resistance' or 'susceptibility' factors are definitely very complex and are greatly overshadowed by the environmental influences. This is clearly shown by the enormous drop of about 95 per cent in the tuberculosis death rate in the United States during the past fifty years as health, living conditions, and medical care have greatly improved. At the same time, the tuberculosis rate remains quite high wherever environments continue to be unfavourable. Thus, while persons in whose families tuberculosis has appeared should be especially on guard against possible symptoms, the danger of the disease's developing will be very small if living conditions, diet, and medical care are adequate.

Polio (*poliomyelitis*, or *infantile paralysis*) is another disease that is basically environmental, resulting from a virus infection. But it also appears that degrees of resistance or susceptibility to the disease may be hereditary, perhaps through recessive genes. For one thing, it was found that if one of two identical twins contracted polio, the risk of the other's developing the disease was perhaps six times as great as that when the other of a pair of twins was fraternal.

CHAPTER THIRTEEN

OUTER DEFECTS AND ABNORMALITIES

MOST RECOGNIZABLE OF the human defects and abnormalities are, of course, those which strike our eyes instantly – unusual sizes and shapes of bodies, peculiarities in bodily details, odd skin conditions, etc. Many of these are inherited, in some cases appearing at birth, but often not until much later. But there are also many similar abnormalities which are purely or mostly due to environmental mishaps or deficiencies in prenatal life. Lack of sufficient oxygen or of needed chemical elements for the developing baby may be among the causes. Very often an environmental abnormality is mistakenly thought to be hereditary, and sometimes the reverse is true; or it may be hereditary in one family but environmental in another. A knowledge of the facts is especially important to persons who have had close relatives or children with any one of the conditions to be described.

Let us look first at the *stature abnormalities.* Human nature tends to be so fairly uniform that a difference of a foot or so above or below the average height range is apt to be considered abnormal. As noted in Chapter 10, human beings as groups have never been deliberately bred to produce extremes in size. Even if this were attempted, it is doubtful if we could produce breeds of healthy humans averaging more than about 7 feet 6 inches tall, or smaller than 3 feet 6 inches to 4 feet. At least that is suggested by such degrees of human stature as have so far appeared.

Dwarfs are of several types, with heredity working differently to produce each. *Midgets* ('Lilliputians', or *ateliotic* dwarfs) are the doll-like persons with normal proportions who do not reach beyond about 3 feet 7 inches in height. (The smallest adult midget on record was 21 inches.) Failure to grow taller results from an inherited deficiency in the pituitary,

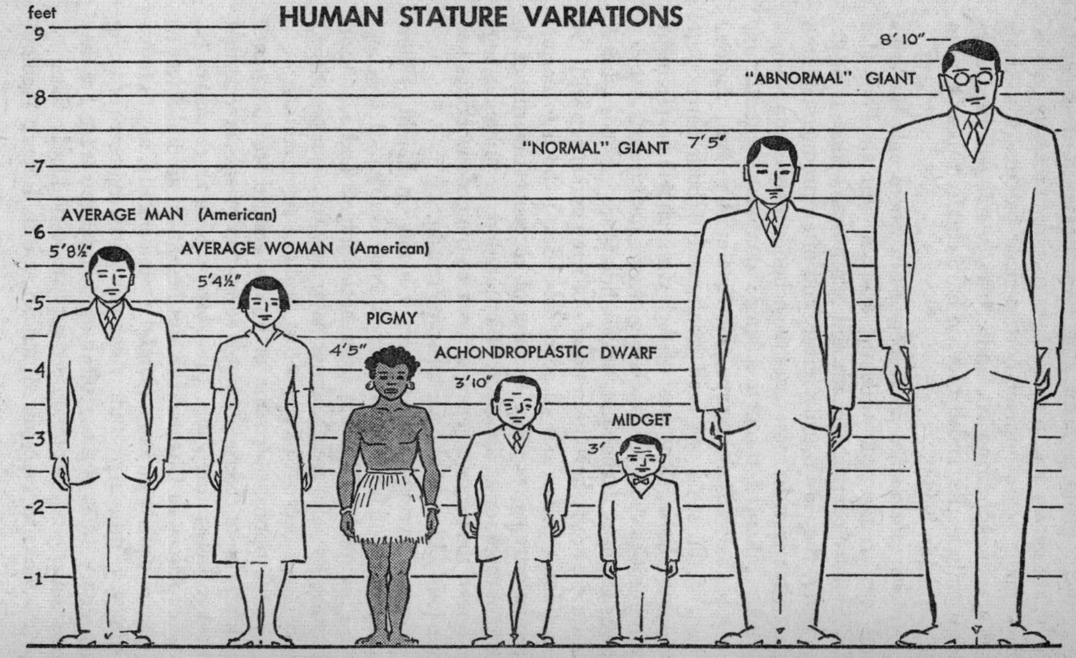

* For British averages, see page 75, footnote.

or 'growth' gland, probably due in most cases to two separate dominant genes, and in some cases to simple recessive genes. Most midgets are born of normal-sized parents (sometimes two or more appearing in a family) because midgets themselves are usually sterile, and if they do have children these tend to be normal in height.

Achondroplastic dwarfs are persons in whom only the arms and legs are stunted, while the trunk is normal. They also usually have oversized hands and pug noses. Unlike midgets, however, they are usually fertile, and often produce children like themselves. In most cases the achondroplastic condition is directly inherited through a single dominant gene: if one parent is a dwarf of this type, there is almost an even chance a child of the same type will result, and if both parents are achondroplastic, all or most of their children will be. (In many communities there are whole families of such dwarfs. Among lower animals, dachshunds and bulldogs are achondroplastic, and there are or have been breeds of cows and sheep with the condition.) Sometimes an achondroplastic is born to normal human parents, possibly because of recessive inheritance in certain cases; or as the result of a mutation, or sudden change in one of the parent's genes; or because the gene workings had previously been held back for some reason.

Pygmies average about 4 feet 6 inches in height. Whole tribes of them are found in Africa, New Guinea, Malaya, and the Philippines. Differing from both midgets and achondroplastics, Pygmies are not abnormal in any way, but are merely undersized because of genes that produce small stature.

At the opposite extreme of human nature are the *giants*. Tallness up to a certain point – seven feet or so – is inherited through tall-stature genes, probably working as recessives (as was explained in Chapter 10). But heights of around 8 feet or over are usually due to a glandular abnormality, most often a 'runaway' pituitary gland, which gives little evidence of being hereditary. Most of these 'pituitary' giants grow weaker as they grow taller, and usually do not survive beyond early maturity. (In the record case, an American youth, Robert Wadlow, reached 8 feet 9½ inches when he died at age 22, in 1940. However, another American, Clifford M. Thompson, who was well over 8 feet, reached the age of 51 and was apparently vigorous when he died in 1955, reportedly from a disease.)

Extreme fatness, as in circus 'fat ladies' (and men of the same type), may very well be due to a metabolic disorder. The record for a fat woman is 55 stone, 2 lbs; for a fat man, 71 stone, 6 lbs. Whether heredity plays any part in these extreme conditions is uncertain. Although extremely fat women

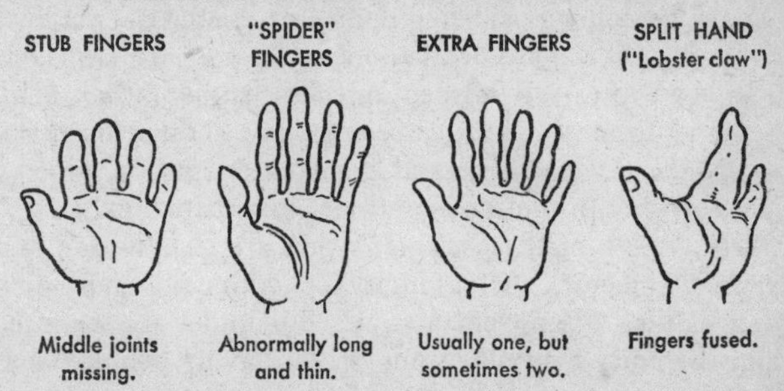

NOTE: Any one of the above hand conditions may be accompanied by a similar condition in the feet of the individual. All are dominant or partly dominant in inheritance. (See text.)

sometimes have similar daughters, a prenatal glandular influence in the mother may be responsible. (Diabetic women, for instance, may produce abnormally fat babies.)

Inherited *hand and foot abnormalities* are of many kinds, almost all due to dominant or dominant-qualified genes. Thus, the conditions are markedly noticeable in families, since wherever a parent has one of these abnormalities, the odds may be up to fifty-fifty that any of the children will have the same abnormality, or some variation of it. Often the abnormality also appears in the feet or toes. Most common of these conditions are stub fingers (*brachyphalangy*); extra fingers (and/or toes); 'claw' or 'split' hand (and/or foot); webbed fingers (and/or toes); 'spider' hand (abnormally long, thin fingers and/or toes); and stiff fingers, with fused joints. Other inherited conditions include missing fingers or thumbs, double-joints; paddle-shaped thumbs; and misshapen toes.

Clubfoot in only some cases may, perhaps, result from an inherited tendency, and if so, it would be through recessive genes. But in many, if not most instances, prenatal accidents appear to be responsible.

In the body proper, there are many skeletal peculiarities for which heredity can be responsible (once environmental factors have been ruled out). Included among the inherited conditions (with the gene involved being dominant-qualified – not always showing its effects) are brittle bones (*blue sclerotic*, revealed by bluish eyewhites); deformed or cleft spine (*spina bifida*); cobbler's ('funnel') chest; extreme hollow chest; 'tower skull' (*oxycephaly*, *acrocephaly*); and cranial soft-spot, in which the infant soft spot in the skull continues into maturity.

Teeth defects, of the common types, are usually due to environmental factors, such as improper tooth care, faulty diet or eating habits, water elements, etc. But under the same conditions heredity may play some part in giving people good or bad teeth, or well-formed or misshapen teeth. Where heredity can be suspected most strongly is in the case of specific teeth defects or peculiarities that reappear in members of the same family in succeeding generations, and under different conditions. Some of the abnormalities that can be inherited are missing teeth of one kind or another; extra teeth; and defective enamel. *Malocclusion* – the improper adjustment of the upper to the lower teeth – usually appears due to faulty chewing habits, but heredity may sometimes be involved.

Cleft palate and *harelip* (together or separate) may be produced by different factors, hereditary and environmental, or both. Even where there is a hereditary tendency (believed to be in about 20 per cent of the cases), the appearance of the defect may still often depend on adverse factors in the baby's prenatal environment. As a mother grows older, the risk of having a child with harelip and cleft palate increases.

Skin defects are usually acquired disorders, due to internal diseases or outside irritants. Less frequently are skin disorders and defects hereditary.

Albinism is one of the most striking of the skin abnormalities. While previously discussed under eye and hair colouring, it is mainly a defect in skin pigmentation, which also affects the other pigmenting processes, as well as producing other defects. Albinism is found in one degree or another in almost all living things, both plants and animals. Among human beings the most prevalent type (occurring in Negroes and Mongolians, as well as whites) is probably inherited through recessive genes, but additional genes may also be involved. The highest incidence of albinos (7 per 1,000), is among the San Blas Indians of central Panama. Moderate types of skin pigment deficiency – albinoidism, 'piebald' skin, or 'white blaze' (a patch of white hair above the centre of the forehead) – may also be hereditary, usually through dominant or dominant-qualified genes.

Birthmarks may sometimes be hereditary. The only ones that need cause concern are a few rare hereditary types discussed under 'Cancer', and certain other precancerous birthmarks – seldom if ever hereditary – which are a combination of smooth, hairless, pigmented, and not raised, or which suddenly begin to turn black, grow, or bleed. The common type of birthmarks – which are *not harmful* – are those raised, warty, and hairy. Often they are purely environmental, but where hereditary are dominated. A birthmark oddity is the *Mongolian spot*, a temporary bluish patch near the base of the spine, which appears in almost all infants of Mongolian stock, in many Negro infants, and sometimes in darker-skinned white infants.

Other hereditary skin conditions include *abnormal blistering* of various types, fatty skin growths (*xanthoma*, *xanthelasma*) on the eyelids or elsewhere; horny skin, or scaly or 'fish' skin (*icthyosis*); 'elephant' skin, a form of cracked skin, often fatal in early life, which is recessive in inheritance; and 'rubber' skin, a freak elastic skin. *Psoriasis*, when it runs in families, may have a hereditary basis (dominant-qualified or recessive).

Sweat-gland defects – the inability to sweat – can be inherited, mostly in males, through a sex-linked gene, or if mild in form, may be dominant.

Defective hair and nails are frequently hereditary. There are various types of these: (1) the downy, fine hair of infancy remaining through life; (2) a beady type of hair (*monilethrix*), present at birth and continuing to grow that way; (3) freakish, excessively long, soft hair on the face and elsewhere, with other effects, appearing at puberty, and found mostly in some French-Canadian families. All the the foregoing conditions are either dominant or partly so in inheritance.

Since the nails and hair are fashioned of much the same substances, certain of the hereditary nail abnormalities accompany some of the hair conditions, such as (1) and (4), mentioned above. But some other nail defects and abnormalities are inherited independently. These include: absent nails, thick and protruding nails, spotted, bluish-white nails, milky-white nails, thickened nails (with thick skin on palms and soles, also) and thin nails (small and soft, or flat). All the foregoing are usually dominant or dominant qualified; but absent nails may also be recessive.

Baldness is by far the most common of the hair defects that have a hereditary basis. The ordinary, widespread type of baldness that comes to about two in five mature and older men is probably hereditary in the great majority of cases. In these, falling hair, and sometimes its almost total loss, appear to be unrelated to any disease, state of bodily health, or local scalp disorder. Nor is there any truth in the old theory that men become bald and women do not because over the ages men have cut their hair, or taken less care of it than have women. (As previously noted, the habit of ancestors could have no effect on their descendants' inherited traits.) The explanation for the sex differences in baldness, offered by geneticists, is that the baldness tendency results from a special kind of gene, called sex-influenced or sex-limited because the strength of its effects is governed, or limited, mostly by the sex of the person receiving it. Thus, only *one* of these baldness genes can produce baldness in a male, whereas in a female a single gene has virtually no effect, and even two of the genes may produce only a thinning of the hair, or no more than mild baldness. One specific reason seems to be that the male hormones stimulate the baldness gene to do its work, whereas the female hormones counteract its effects. Backing up this theory are the findings that baldness rarely, if ever, develops in *eunuchs* – castrated males lacking the normal supply of male hormones – even if

Inherited "Pattern" Baldness

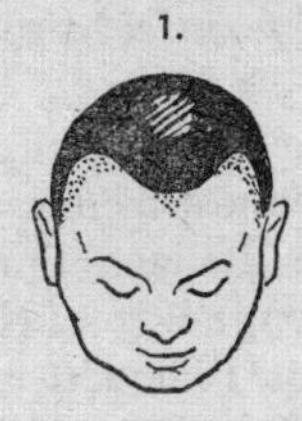

1. Noticeable loss of hair at forehead, temples and sides. Also, in older men, small bald spot in crown.

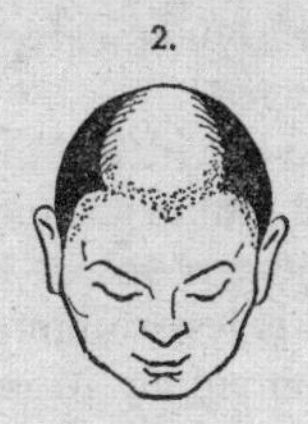

2. Much of hair lost from the forehead to the crown.

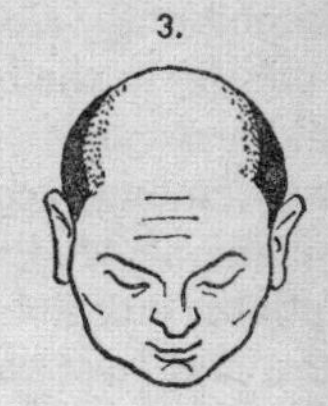

3. Only sparse hair over ears, and in a fringe around the back.

NOTE: Different degrees of baldness, as shown, may run in families. Among women, hair loss rarely goes beyond stage No. 1. (See text.)

they have the inherited baldness genes. But if these same males are given doses of male hormones to make up for their deficiency, baldness develops in those with the inherited tendencies, though not in the others.

The above facts should dispose of the old notion that a heavy head of hair in a man indicates virility and potency, while lack of hair suggests the contrary. Actually, once the baldness gene is present, it is the more 'feminine' and less virile man (deficient in male hormones) who is apt to retain his hair, whereas it is the more 'masculine' man (most abundant in male hormones) who is likely to become bald. But all this applies only to the effects of hormones on the workings of the baldness gene. Otherwise, the fact that a man is or isn't bald proves nothing as to his manliness.

Here, then, is how heredity works in baldness: if a young man's father was, or is, bald, there is at least an even chance he himself also will be. The threat is increased if there also was or is baldness on his mother's side (her father, brothers, etc.), since a son may have received a baldness gene from his mother, even though she herself has shown none of the effects. There are indications that the baldness genes and their effects in some families are stronger than in other families. Thus, degrees of hereditary baldness appear to range from almost total hair loss, beginning to develop in early maturity, to only partial hair loss or thinning in the older ages.

Baldness genes also give evidence of being distributed differently among races and ethnic groups. The most baldness is found among Mediterranean peoples – Greeks, Italians, Turks, Egyptians, etc. Baldness is less common among Negroes than whites, and least common among Mongolians. (The latter, at the same time, also have less facial and body hair than whites.)

In only a minority of cases does baldness result from such environmental causes as infectious diseases, glandular and nervous ailments, diabetes or fevers, which may produce temporary or permanent hair loss. But medical authorities refute the claims of so-called 'baldness institutes' that common baldness is caused by dandruff, oiliness of the scalp, or simple scalp diseases, and that clearing up these disorders will cure or prevent baldness and restore hair growth. Up to the time of writing no cure for ordinary, inherited baldness has been found, and in the United States advertising such a cure is forbidden by law.

In infrequent instances the normal processes of sex determination and development (discussed in Chapter 4) can be upset or swerved so as to produce *sex abnormalities* of various types. These may include abnormalities (1) in the sex organs; (2) in the secondary sex characteristics (body form, hair growth, breasts, etc.); (3) in the stages of sexual development (greatly speeded up, or much retarded); and (4) in sexual and reproductive functioning. Often these conditions are caused by environmental factors – developmental mishaps, glandular upsets, or diseases – usually in prenatal life but sometimes in early childhood. However, hereditary defects, or abnormalities in the genetic mechanism of sex determination, are involved in a number of conditions.

A remarkable recent finding has been that two of the more common forms of incomplete sexual development are due to abnormalities in the pairing of the sex chromosomes. Normally, it will be recalled, a fertilized egg has either two X's, producing a female, or an X and Y, producing a male. But in unusual instances there may be (a) two X's coupled with a Y – an XXY combination; or (b) just one X by itself – an XO egg. In either case normal sex development is impeded. The XXY combination results in a condition called the *Klinefelter syndrome*, in which the individual, while male (because of the presence of the Y), does not achieve full masculine development in his reproductive organs or other physical respects. In the second case (b), known as the *Turner syndrome*, the XO egg results in an incompletely developed female who in all but a few instances known grows up lacking functioning ovaries and mature breasts. In addition, the 'Turner' as well as the 'Klinefelter' individuals are often mentally retarded and may have other abnormalities. (Also to be found are rare XXX, XXXX, and XXXY individuals, all defective in various ways.)

Hermaphroditism is another general kind of sex abnormality in which the individual is in some degree 'in between' in sexual development, with at least partially formed organs and/or sex characteristics of both male and female. This condition may result if the XX or XY sex-chromosome and sex-mechanism workings are deranged or impeded, usually in prenatal life, so that the individual's development is not thrown clearly in either sex direction. But only in very rare instances is the individual actually 'half male and half female', with both testes and ovaries, and what may pass as a vagina and a penis. (Nor is any case known of such a human hermaphrodite who was able to function sexually and reproductively as both a male and a female.) Much more common – about one in a thousand persons – are the *pseudo-hermaphrodites*, individuals who are mainly of one sex, with either testes or ovaries, but with outer details of the opposite sex organs sufficiently pronounced so that mistakes may often be made in classifying their sex at birth or later. Whether inherited defects are involved in partial or complete hermaphroditism is uncertain, but there is a possibility that some of the cases which appear to run in families may be due to recessive genes.

Where a person's true, or genetic, sex is not clearly revealed by surface sex characteristics and is in doubt, it is now possible to clear up uncertainties by *sex identity tests*. These involve making microscopic examinations of some of the person's cells, which will then show whether they have the XX chromosome combination (of a genetic female), or the XY combination (of a genetic male). In one of these tests, devised by Dr Murray L. Barr of Canada, the investigator looks for a little blob of 'chromatin' (chromosome fibres) in each cell, produced by two X's together, and which can be seen in most of the cells of a genetic female. (See illustration.) In another type of test, where white blood cells are examined, the two X's reveal themselves by a peculiar 'drumstick' formation in the chromosome mass, not found where there is only one X coupled with a Y. The best test, but one more difficult to make, involves taking certain cells of the body (such as those from bone marrow or the skin or the white cells of the blood), and treating them in a way which causes the chromosomes to become easily seen. This clearly shows exactly how many and what sex chromosomes or other chromosomes the individual carries, and whether there are any abnormalities in the chromosome combinations.

Is *sex-changing* possible after a person has developed as a male or a female? Sensational cases have indeed been reported from time to time of 'men transformed into women', or vice versa. In lower animals this is possible, and in some species occurs in the natural state. Thus, the oyster alternates from being a male one season to being a female the next. In poultry,

SEX IDENTITY TESTS*

A. "CHROMATIN" TEST

Female cell | Male cell

"Chromatin positive" mass

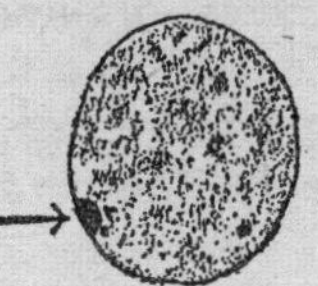

At left, typical female cell (scraped from inside of cheek) has a little "chromatin" mass at rim of the nucleus, formed by two X's. Male cell, right, lacks this mass.

B. THE "DRUMSTICK" TEST

Female cell | Male cell

"Drumstick-shaped" mass

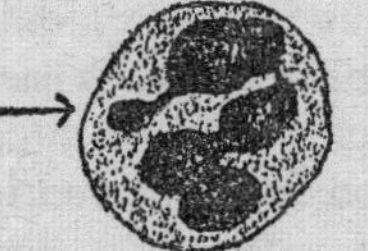

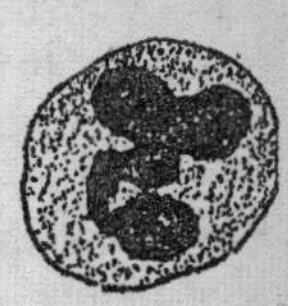

At left, typical female cell (from white blood cells) shows a "drumstick" formation made by the two X's. Male cell, right, with only one X, does not have the drumstick.

(*Illustrations drawn from microphotographs A., top, by Drs. Murray L. Barr and Keith L. Moore; B., bottom, by Drs. Donald K. Briggs and Herbert S. Kupperman.)

where sex is not as strongly fixed as in humans, hormonal upsets may sometimes cause a hen to develop into a rooster. However, these radical sex reversals have not been found possible in human beings. Most of the reported cases of human sex-changing involved pseudo-hermaphrodites who were operated on to correct abnormalities. The more highly publicized cases of recent years, of physically normal males who claimed to have been turned into females, involved nothing more, according to medical reports, than plastic operations by which the outer male sex organs were removed and female organs simulated.

Operations are sometimes also essential to correct congenital defects in the sex organs of boys which may have a hereditary basis. In one condition, *hypospadias*, there is a slit or misplaced opening in the underside of the penis. This condition is sometimes hereditary through a partly dominant gene, but may also be non-hereditary. In *cryptorchidism* the testes fail to descend into the scrotum. While usually due to non-hereditary prenatal mishaps, it may possibly be hereditary (recessive) in some cases.

In contrast to impeded or incomplete sex development in either sex, there may be an abnormal speeding up of the process, known as *pubertas praecox* – or precocious puberty – a tendency to which runs in some families. In extreme cases puberty may begin in girls or boys as early as age three or four. These cases are usually due to glandular upsets or tumours, but where the condition has appeared in successive members of a family for several generations, the possibility of inheritance arises, although the method is in doubt. (A case reported in 1953 was of a Texas boy who at age three had achieved technical puberty and was 'producing fertile sperms, and whose father, grandfather, and great-grandfather and several other male relatives had also shown extremely premature sexual development, with no evidence of other abnormalities.)

Another unusual aspect of sex development is that *sterility* can be inherited in certain cases through hidden recessive genes carried by normal parents and coming together in a child. In other cases sterility may result from any of various hereditary conditions that affect the sex organs and prevent the production of fertile eggs or sperms. Some types of sterility go with inherited glandular and chemical deficiencies that affect the body as a whole. Other types (rarer) may produce no outward abnormalities and no detectable symptoms other than lack of fertile sperms in the male; or, in the female, inability to produce fertile eggs or to conceive. It might be noted that sterility usually goes also with two of the conditions previously described, the Klinefelter's and Turner's syndromes, although these, while due to chromosome abnormalities, are not known to be hereditary.

CHAPTER FOURTEEN

DEFECTS IN SENSES AND BODY FUNCTIONS

HEREDITY PRODUCES or helps to produce hundreds of eye defects, from very mild ones to those causing total blindness. Possibly one fifth of the blindness cases are hereditary, four fifths environmental. More than half of the blindness in young people results from prenatal or later mishaps, such as diseases, infections, or dietary deficiencies. But about one eighth of the cases of *congenital* blindness are due to defective genes that fail to construct properly some vital part of the eye mechanism – the iris, retina, eye nerves, etc. In addition, a considerable proportion of the cases of blindness which develop at later stages, in childhood, maturity, or old age, are also the result of defective eye genes.

Colour blindness is the most common of the inherited eye defects, and also of the conditions that afflict particularly males (about eight times as many as females). Ordinary colour blindness is the inability to distinguish the *colour* difference between red and green, although, as with red and green traffic lights, the afflicted person might still recognize their difference in shade or intensity. About 4 per cent of white American males have the common form of colour blindness, while another 4 per cent suffer from lesser deficiencies in red–green colour vision, or other colour vision. Among Negro males there is only about half this incidence of colour blindness, and among American Indians only about one quarter. Whether any cases of red–green colour blindness are due to environmental factors, such as possibly a vitamin A deficiency, is uncertain. (It may be noted that virtually all lower animals, with the exception of monkeys and apes – man's closest animal relatives – are colour blind either wholly or to a great extent.) To date no cure for ordinary colour blindness is known, although training may increase a colour-blind person's ability to distinguish the shade differences between colours.

In its inheritance workings, colour blindness follows the principles of simple sex-linked inheritance (see Chapter 11), in which one colour-blindness gene produces the defect in males, but two genes are needed to produce the defect in females. Since the colour-blindness gene is in the X chromosome, and a male can receive this chromosome only from his mother, it is only by way of their mothers that males can inherit colour blindness. For a female to be colour-blind, both the X's she receives – the one from her father and the one from her mother – must carry the colour-blindness gene, which means that her *father must be colour-blind* and her mother must be a carrier for the gene. Some women who are carriers, with a single such gene, may show it by a slight defect in red–green colour vision if their normal gene does not completely counteract the effects of the defective one.

Other visual deficiencies in which heredity often, but not always, may play a part, include *extreme nearsightedness*, and *extreme farsightedness*, and also, possibly, *astigmatism*. Various gene mechanisms may be involved in these conditions. *Cross-eyes* is sometimes hereditary, sometimes not. Two eye diseases, *night blindness* (the inability to see in dim light), and *day blindness* (failing eyesight in bright daylight), definitely have a hereditary basis. Night blindness has different methods of inheritance, depending on the type. Day blindness is usually recessive.

Cataracts, among the most common of serious eye diseases, are hereditary in some cases, in others not. Most cataracts in children, and many which develop in early maturity or middle age, are probably hereditary. But it should be clear that some congenital cataracts result from prenatal infections or acquired diseases; and that many cataracts of later life also may be due mainly to diseases and infections, as well as to ageing effects. Before concluding that a cataract in any given case is hereditary, the family history must be known. In many families successive cataracts which are very similar in type, severity, and age of onset point strongly to the action of dominant-qualified genes.

Glaucoma, when occurring in adults and linked with other eye defects, may not be hereditary in most cases; but, in many families, there is considerable evidence that primary glaucoma (not linked to other eye diseases) is inherited, possibly through dominant or sex-linked genes. Rarer inherited forms of glaucoma may also occur in infants and in children (mostly boys).

Mirror-Reading and Writing

An inherited oddity

Afflicted persons see and write upside down and backwards. (To see what the boy above has written, hold illustration before a mirror and look at it with your head turned down.)

Other serious hereditary eye diseases are *retinitis pigmentosa*, in which the retina fills with pigment; several forms of *optic atrophy*, where the optic nerve withers, causing blindness; and *retinoblastoma* or *glioma retinae*, a very rare congenital cancer of the eye. Also among hereditary eye afflictions are *defective corneas*, *lenses*, and *irises* of various kinds; *quivering eyeballs* (*nystagmus*); *dry eyes*, in which the tear glands are blocked or constricted; abnormally *small eyes* (*microphthalmos*); and *drooping eyelids* (*ptosis*), in which the eyes always appear to be half-closed. Many of the foregoing conditions, or some types of these conditions, can be dominant or partly-dominant in inheritance. Special mention might be made of an inherited visual oddity, *mirror-reading and writing*, depicted in the accompanying illustration. This is dominant-qualified in inheritance.

Deafness may have some hereditary basis – direct or indirect – in anywhere from 10 to 35 per cent of the cases. The exact facts are difficult to establish because diseases and accidents may often play such a large part in causing deafness, and unless clear medical records of previous afflicted members of a family are available, conclusions cannot be drawn about hereditary deafness risks to succeeding members.

Congenital deafness can be produced in babies prenatally by various diseases in the mother (German measles, syphilis, etc.) or, following birth, by meningitis, scarlet fever, mumps, etc. But perhaps one third of the cases of congenital deafness in the United States are hereditary, resulting from failure of certain genes to control construction of the inner-ear mechanism properly. If a child is born deaf it is especially serious because inability to hear also interferes greatly with learning to speak. In former times this almost always doomed the congenitally deaf child to be a *mute* as well (hence the common use of the term deaf-mute), but today special training helps many deaf children to speak.

The manner in which congenital deafness might be inherited is still uncertain, but it is believed generally due to recessive genes, plus other factors – possibly additional defective genes, or certain adverse influences in prenatal life. This is suggested by the fact that in many cases where both parents were congenitally deaf, children with normal hearing resulted. Generally, however, deaf parents whose condition has not been caused by accident or disease have a much greater than average risk of producing deaf children, especially if they are closely related and are carrying the same genes.

Middle-ear deafness (*otosclerosis*) is the most common of the serious hearing defects that develop in the more mature years, more often among women than men, and especially after childbirth. Some cases of adult deafness result from injuries and infections, but the hereditary type of middle-ear deafness is caused by a deposit of bony obstruction inside the ear. The genes responsible are usually dominant, but in some instances are recessive. An operation to open the obstruction in the inner ear often greatly improves hearing. *Inner-ear*, or *nerve deafness*, which also comes on usually in middle age, is dominant.

There is much uncertainty as to hereditary factors in any of the common *speech defects*, such as stuttering or lisping (when not related to cleft palate or to hereditary nerve and muscle disorders). Many psychologists maintain that stuttering or stammering in a child results mostly from some emotional or psychological disturbance. (Adults, too, may develop speech disorders under stress.) However, certain facts remain puzzling: (1) under the same conditions only some persons will develop the stuttering habit; (2) stuttering may run in families even when individual members have not been in contact with one another; (3) the incidence of speech defects among males is at least five times that among females, with no proof that this all due to differences in emotional stresses; and (4) among identical twins, if one stutters the other also does almost invariably, which is not so among fraternal twins. Some authorities believe, therefore, that heredity cannot be ruled out as a *predisposing* factor in speech defects. But if there are any genes involved, they have not yet been identified.

With regard to left-handedness and stuttering, despite the wide belief that these are connected, recent evidence indicates that the proportion of 'lefties' among stutterers is not perceptibly higher than the general average. The U.S. Army estimates are that 8·6 per cent of men drafted for service – almost one in eleven – are left-handed.

Muscle and nerve disorders, if not due to accidents, may sometimes be hereditary. This applies to some of the *ataxias* (including *Friedreich's* and *Marie's cerebellar*); certain types of paralysis, including *spastic paraplegia* and *family periodic paralysis*; and some types of *muscular atrophy* and *muscular dystrophy*. However, one must be extremely careful not to confuse the hereditary muscular or nerve defects with similar types that are due solely to accidents, injuries, or diseases, whether before birth or after. In any case, only after a given condition has been properly diagnosed by a competent specialist should any conclusions be drawn about its hereditary basis.

Epilepsy is also among the conditions that can be caused in various ways. Many authorities now believe that heredity is not involved in the majority of cases of epilepsy, but that in a certain percentage (perhaps 25 per cent or more), heredity does produce some *predisposition* or *tendency* – that is, an inherent weakness in the brain or nervous systems which can lead to epileptic symptoms under unfavourable conditions. These conditions may include accidents and injuries (before birth or after), diseases, metabolic disorders, brain and nerve tumors, etc. The assumption might be, then, that some individuals start off with a nervous system sufficiently unbalanced, because of defective genes, to make them much more likely than average persons to become epileptic under a given environmental 'push'. Recent findings indicate that persons carrying such genes may be identified through abnormal ('epileptoid') brain patterns. There is also the tentative theory (not yet proved) that one or a pair of these genes may produce the abnormal brain waves without other effects, but that a double dose of the same genes may produce epilepsy or the tendency to it. However, only one rare condition – *myoclonic epilepsy* (differing in many ways from the ordinary types) – has so far been proved directly hereditary, through recessive genes.

Various studies further indicate that (1) among identical twins, if one is epileptic, the other will also show an abnormal brain-wave pattern and will be epileptic in about 70 per cent of the cases, whereas among fraternal twins both are epileptic only a fourth as often; (2) among close relatives of epileptics the incidence of epilepsy is about five times that in the general population; (3) the abnormal 'epileptoid' brain waves seem to run strongly in certain families, and if a child is epileptic, the 'epileptoid' brain waves will appear in one parent, if not both.

In the large majority of cases there is no relationship between epilepsy and intelligence. About two thirds of the epileptics are average or above average in IQ; about 23 per cent are slightly below average, and only 10 per cent are retarded sufficiently to be placed in institutions. Epileptics most likely to be mentally defective are those whose conditions result from brain injuries and not from any inherited tendencies.

In another category of ailments are the hereditary *biochemical disorders*. Some of the more serious types have been previously discussed (Chapter 12) or will be dealt with later (blood conditions, mental diseases and defects, etc.). Here we will take note of certain other conditions in which genetic 'errors of metabolism' are involved.

Gout, one of the best known biochemical ailments, may result from a hereditary susceptibility towards the production of excess uric acid in the blood (*hyperuricemia*). The susceptibility is caused by a dominant gene, but the disease is much more frequent in males because the male chemical make-up is particularly likely to promote the development of gout, whereas the female chemical environment may help to suppress it.

Also among the genetic metabolic disorders are many urinary conditions, identified by unusual amounts of certain substances in the urine, and by other effects they produce. Usually recessive in inheritance, these conditions include, chiefly, *alkaptanuria*, *porphyrinuria*, *cystinuria*, and *pentosuria*.

Most common of the bodily disturbances – sometimes very serious, but often so mild they may be called merely 'peculiarities' – are the *allergies*. These relate to unfavourable reactions to given foods or drugs and may be due to hereditary deficiencies, or to environmental factors, or to a combination of both. Probably every person is allergic to one or more things, which may be feathers, dust, the fur of a particular animal, or any of hundreds of foods, drinks, drugs, and chemical substances. Frequently allergies result in or are linked with violent hay fever, asthma, or certain skin diseases or digestive disturbances, which in children may interfere with proper growth and development.

It is quite possible that what causes an allergy to become acute may often be some emotional ('psychosomatic') disturbance in the individual which makes the chemical reactions of the body especially sensitive. However, the fact that individuals tend to be allergic only to *particular* substances, and that such allergies, often of a peculiar nature, tend to run in families, strongly suggests that heredity is also involved as an influence or direct cause, perhaps in three fourths of the cases. There is some evidence that allergy inheritance may be dominant. This apparently applies to *migraine headache*, which is sometimes viewed an an allergic condition. Women are afflicted by migraine twice as often as men, the condition appearing to be aggravated by female hormones, and the worst attacks coming during menstrual periods.

CHAPTER FIFTEEN

BLOOD TYPES AND CONDITIONS

As the most vital fluid of the body, blood has been given much careful study. Many important hereditary differences among individuals in their blood elements and blood cells have been found. Some of these blood differences involve abnormalities, deficiencies or diseases with varying consequences, ranging from mild defects to serious and fatal results. Other differences have importance only in certain situations, as in transfusions, when the blood of one individual is mixed with that of another. Discoveries of the blood types and of methods for 'typing' persons have eliminated most of the grave dangers which attended transfusions in former times.

The main blood-type differences among human beings – in the A, B, AB, and O groups – involve the presence or absence of certain chemicals in the red blood cells. The A substance is determined by one dominant gene, the B substance by another dominant gene. In addition, there is an O gene which determines neither substance, and is recessive to the other two genes. Since a person must receive one of these three blood genes from each parent, six paired combinations are possible. A blood will result from either an AA or an AO gene combination (the O gene being recessive). Similarly, B blood will result from either a BB or a BO combination. But if a person receives an A gene from one parent, a B gene from the other parent, AB blood will result, because neither gene dominates the other and both A and B substances are produced. Finally, O blood will result only if an O gene is received from each parent.

In addition to the A-B-O blood substances (and the Rh, to be discussed later), there are a number of less important inherited blood substances. Among them are the M and N substances, inherited through mutually dominant genes, so that a person getting an M gene from one parent, an N gene from the other, would be the M-N type. Other blood substances recently discovered are the so-called S, Kell, Duffy, and Lutheran. Many of these, especially the M-N substances, are of interest so far mainly in disputed paternity cases and in racial studies.

Limited recent evidence also suggests that persons of some blood groups may be somewhat more prone to develop certain diseases than are persons of other blood groups. Such associations are claimed between blood-group O and duodenal ulcer, and between blood-group A and cancer of the stomach, and also, possibly, diabetes in males. Further study of these points is needed before they can be accepted as proved.

The most important application of the A-B-O blood-type findings is in transfusion, for if a person is infused with blood of a different type from his own, there may be a clumping or disintegration of the introduced blood cells. The greatest danger arises if an O-blood person receives blood of any of the other three types; or if an A person is given B blood, or a B person is given A blood. An AB individual can most safely receive blood of other persons. Contrariwise, O blood, lacking A and B substances, can be transfused with least risk into persons of other blood types. But the term 'universal donor', formerly applied to an O person, is no longer used, since any O donor might also be carrying additional blood substances that could be harmful if transfused into another person who lacks them. (Among these substances is the Rh factor, to be discussed presently.)

An important fact to keep in mind is that the blood types of two members of a family may differ through inheritance just as their hair colour, eye colour, or other traits may differ. Thus, where these differences occur, there may be precisely the same danger in transfusing a mother's blood into her own child, or the blood of one brother into another, as in transfusing blood from any unrelated person. On the other hand, the blood of an outsider, even of a different race, can be safely transfused into a person with the same blood type.

The Rh disease (*erythroblastosis fetalis*), now widely known as a blood affliction of certain newborn babies, is produced in prenatal life by hereditary factors working in an indirect way to cause conflict between the baby's blood and the mother's. The disease itself is not inherited, but can develop *only* when the baby's blood carries an inherited chemical substance known as the Rh factor, and the mother's blood lacks this substance, being of the inherited type known as Rh-negative. But even then, there is danger to the baby only in a very small percentage of the cases, for reasons which will become clear when we see the sequence of things which must happen:

1. In the course of prenatal development, some of the baby's red blood cells with the Rh-positive substances must break through the barriers of the placenta and filter into the mother's circulation.

2. The mother's body must respond by producing *antibodies* or anti-Rh counteracting chemicals, to fight off the foreign Rh-positive red blood cells.

3. The Rh antibodies in turn must pass into the baby in sufficient amounts to cause serious injury to his blood cells. Altogether, the serious results may occur in no more than *one in sixteen* of the *one in twelve* cases where the mother is Rh negative and the baby Rh positive – or about one in two hundred pregnancies. Particularly with a *first* baby, the mother's blood will probably not yet have developed enough of the anti-Rh substances to seriously endanger the child. The major threat comes if the mother's blood has started off with anti-Rh substances developed in her through some prior transfusion with Rh-positive blood; or, if this is not her first pregnancy, she previously had carried an Rh-positive baby (or two or more such babies) with whom she had had a blood-substance exchange. (See illustration, page 126.)

The gene that gives rise to the Rh-positive type is dominant; the gene for Rh negative is recessive. Thus, to have Rh-positive blood a person need inherit only one Rh-positive gene. But to have Rh-negative blood a person must receive *two* Rh-negative genes, one from each parent. The relative proportion of positive and negative persons varies with racial groups. Among whites, about 85 per cent are Rh positive, 15 per cent negative. Among American Negroes only 8 per cent are Rh negative, which means the threat of the Rh-disease for their babies is much less than for white babies. Going further, among Chinese, Japanese, and other Mongolians, there are virtually no Rh-negative individuals, almost all being positive, so there is no Rh-disease threat for Mongolian babies unless their parents carry some white genes.

Knowing the facts regarding Rh inheritance, it is now relatively easy to establish in advance whether a given baby of a given couple is threatened by the Rh disease. There is no threat at all (with rare exceptions) if the mother is Rh positive. But if she is Rh negative, the father's blood must immediately be tested. Unless he is among the one in seven (white) who are negative one must go on the assumption that the baby will be positive and that there may be a blood clash with the mother. Thus, the mother must be tested further to see if her blood is already carrying anti-Rh substances, through earlier Rh-positive pregnancies or through transfusions. If she does carry these Rh antibodies, and is already pregnant, the likelihood is that her baby is developing the Rh-disease. Dangers may then be reduced, if a child is born with gravely impaired blood cells, by an immediate blood-exchange process, with all of the defective blood replaced by healthy new blood. With the various precautions now possible or being developed, there is little danger to a first Rh-positive baby of an Rh-negative mother, and only slight danger for a second such baby.*

Adding to the possible mother–child blood conflicts, conditions similar to the Rh disease may sometimes result even

* Credit for the discovery of the Rh factor (in 1939), its method of inheritance, and its role in blood transfusion and the Rh disease, goes mainly to three Americans, Dr Alexander Wiener and Dr Philip Levine, and the late Dr Karl Landsteiner with whom they began their work. Many other experts have since helped in the researches which have led to the saving of thousands of babies yearly.

HOW AN "RH-DISEASE" BABY IS PRODUCED

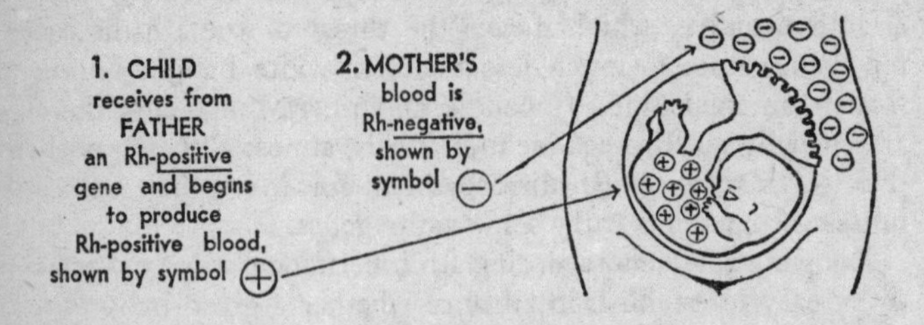

3. Some of the CHILD'S Rh-positive blood substance travels through placenta into MOTHER

4. MOTHER'S blood begins producing ANTIBODIES to attack hostile substance

5. ANTIBODIES FROM MOTHER ENTER CHILD AND BEGIN DESTROYING ITS BLOOD CELLS

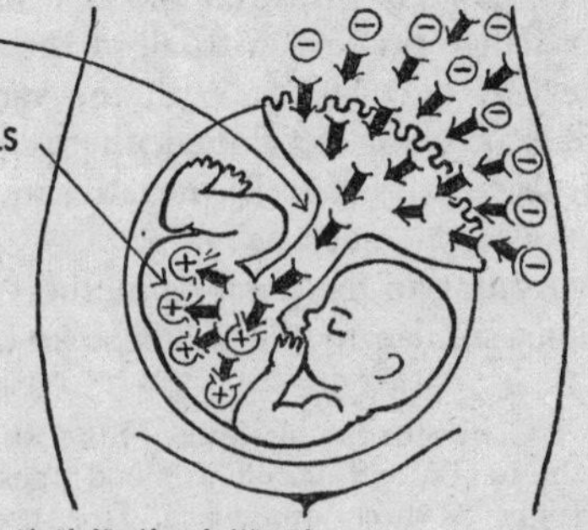

If Rh-negative mother has had previous Rh-positive pregnancies, or transfusions with Rh-positive blood, antibodies already are present.

(Chart prepared with aid of Dr. Alexander Wiener.)

if mother and child are both Rh-positive or both Rh-negative, but have clashing differences in other inherited blood elements. These differences may involve the A, B, and O blood-type substances, and in some instances, certain special Rh elements.

Haemophilia, while comparatively rare, is the best known of the inherited blood diseases, mainly because of its appearance in European royal families. This in turn helped to draw attention to its inheritance as a sex-linked condition, confined almost exclusively to males, and passed along to sons through mothers. As is now clear, haemophilia (which is by no means confined to royalty, but is found in all social levels, nationalities, and races) results from a defect in a gene in the X chromosome concerned with blood clotting, or coagulation. (There are about five varieties of haemophilia, each with a deficiency of a particular compound and with different degrees of severity.)

Since the male receives only one X, and this from his mother, the defective gene for haemophilia will impair his blood-clotting process. But since a female receives two X chromosomes, her other, normal gene, will insure normal blood clotting. For a woman to receive *two* 'haemophilia' genes, it would be necessary for her father to be a haemophiliac and her mother to be a carrier for the 'haemophilia' gene – an extremely unlikely situation. One reason is that most male haemophiliacs have usually died in childhood or early maturity, before they reproduced; another probability is that if a girl baby did receive two 'haemophilia' genes, the double dose would bring death before birth or soon thereafter. Nevertheless, a few cases of women presumably with haemophilia are in the medical records. (The disease has recently been discovered in dogs, where it is inherited as in man. This opens the possibility of new experimental studies leading to remedies.)

In the royal families of Europe the gene for haemophilia appears to have arisen in Queen Victoria, or in her mother, through a mutation – that is, a sudden change. This is the way in which many other 'haemophilia' genes are believed to arise. (Were it not for these new mutations, the 'haemophilia' genes in circulation would eventually be depleted by early deaths of the afflicted males.) Records indicate that Queen Victoria transmitted the gene to four, or possibly five, of nine children, including Leopold, who was a haemophiliac (and perhaps another son, who died in infancy), and three daughters, Victoria, Alice, and Beatrice. These last three 'carriers' passed the gene on to various of their children and grandchildren. Luckily for the present British royal family, Queen Victoria's heir, Edward VII, did not receive the dreaded gene, so that none of his descendants is threatened by the disease. (Although Prince Philip, husband of Queen Elizabeth II, is also a descendant of Queen Victoria, he, too, is free of the 'haemophilia' gene.)

Agammaglobulinaemia is another recently discovered blood deficiency inherited by males, like haemophilia, through a sex-linked recessive gene. The afflicted males lack *serum gamma globulin* and so cannot produce protective antibodies in their blood against various infections and diseases. Formerly they would usually die in childhood but can now be kept alive with antibiotics and gamma globulin.

Most common of the inherited blood diseases are the anaemias, which involve deficiencies in the quantity or nature of the blood, resulting from diseases, infections, or malnutrition. However, a number of types are directly due to inherited abnormalities in the blood cells. Two of these widely known conditions, *Mediterranean* (*Cooley's*) *anaemia*, and 'sickle-cell' anaemia (unrelated to one another), are of particular interest because each is largely confined to persons of specific racial groups, and because of their unusual method of inheritance. In both of these conditions (as Dr James V. Neel has shown), one semi-dominant gene produces certain mild effects; a double dose – two of the same genes – produces extremely serious effects. Fortunately, the mild effects caused by a single gene make it easy to identify the persons carrying it and provide ample forewarning of the dangers of prospective children if two such carriers marry.

Mediterranean anaemia is so called because it is found mostly among persons of Mediterranean stock – Greeks, Italians,

Armenians, etc. (although it also occurs in South-east Asia). The dominant gene responsible produces only mild blood abnormalities if inherited from just one parent. But if a child receives two of the genes, one from each parent, there will be very serious effects in the entire system, including skeletal abnormalities, Mongoloid features, and disturbances which usually bring death in childhood.

Sicklaemia and *sickle-cell* anaemia, conditions which afflict chiefly Negroes, are also inherited by the semi-dominant method. A single gene, from one parent, will cause the mild condition of 'sicklaemia', in which a small percentage of the red cells may show a peculiar, twisted 'sickle' shape, but with the individual otherwise normal. However, two of the same genes – one from each parent – will cause a high proportion (half or more) of the red blood cells to have the abnormality, and to be so defective that fatal anaemia may result. The mild and harmless one-gene condition of sicklaemia occurs in close to 10 per cent of the American Negroes (and 15 per cent or more of those in Africa). Not only is this condition harmless, but recent studies indicate that it may help to provide resistance against malaria, and may be one reason why the malaria incidence is much lower among Negroes than whites in the same environments. The serious double-gene anaemia occurs in about one in three hundred Negroes. Here again, as with 'Mediterranean' anaemia, the incidence of the serious disease can be greatly reduced if persons with the easily recognized one-gene condition avoid marrying similar carriers.

Pernicious anaemia is a chronic, serious blood disease of maturity, due to a defect in the stomach lining, often running in families. Its method of inheritance is not clear, but may possibly be recessive or incompletely dominant. The disease is considerably more common among whites than among Asiatics and Negroes. Children and other close young relatives of a pernicious-anaemia sufferer run a much higher than average chance of developing the condition. Early detection of symptoms may prevent the more serious results.

Among other types of hereditary anaemias are *congenital haemolytic anaemia* (or *acholuric family jaundice*), an anaemia with abnormal, fragile blood cells, and *polycythemia* (*erythremia*), excessive production of red blood cells and blood. Some of the other inherited blood-cell anomalies have no harmful effects. These include *oval-shaped*, or elongated red corpuscles, and undeveloped white blood cells.

CHAPTER SIXTEEN

MENTAL DISEASES

FEARS OF 'inheriting insanity' are probably greater than those regarding any other type of affliction, and go back to earliest human history. First, it should be clear that insanity is now only a popular term, applied to mental diseases without distinguishing one from the other. But actually, as modern psychiatry has shown, there are many types of mental diseases, different in their symptoms and causes. This is especially true with respect to hereditary factors or influences. In some conditions – mostly the rarer ones – heredity plays a direct and major role; in others it produces tendencies or susceptibilities, which will give way to insanity only if there is some strong, adverse environmental push.

In any case, in each type of mental disease heredity may work in a different way and in a different degree. Accordingly, wherever persons fear that they or their children are threatened by insanity because it has appeared previously in their family, they must be careful to establish the type of mental disease with which they are concerned, and then note how heredity may be involved.

But before taking up the mental diseases separately, a few special points should be made clear: roughly, close to one in every twelve persons in the United States* is, or will be at one time or another, afflicted by some mental disease requiring hospitalization. Does this mean that *every* person has an up to one-in-twelve risk of becoming insane? No. For some individuals there may be almost no risk; for others it may be considerably higher than one in twelve – in rare instances up to fifty-five. The risk in each case is determined by the nature of the mental disease, the relative influences of heredity and environment, the age at which the condition usually

* The same proportion in Britain (Institute of Psychiatry, London).

appears, and the individual's own make-up, habits, and experiences.

'*Are people becoming crazier because of modern pressures?*' This is hard to answer. Although there are now vastly more people in mental institutions than there formerly were, there are many reasons for this: mental cases are diagnosed more quickly and expertly; the facilities for taking care of the mentally sick have enormously increased, so many more people can be put in mental hospitals; lengthening life spans have swelled the numbers of mentally ill old people; and the mental casualties of two terrible World Wars have added thousands of others. Yet it also is possible that the complex conditions and pressures of modern life have made it more likely for mental diseases to develop in unstable persons. One can only guess about this, since there are no accurate medical data from former times with which to make comparisons. Similarly, one can draw no conclusions about the incidence of insanity in the United States as compared with other countries, or among those of one race or ethnic group compared with another, so long as the facilities for detecting and caring for the mentally ill differ so greatly. However, in most advanced countries, such as England, Sweden, and Denmark, the proportion of mentally ill is much the same as in the United States. Moreover, wherever psychiatrists have investigated, even among the most isolated primitive peoples living under the simplest conditions, they have found many cases of mental illness, which again strengthens the belief that the inborn tendencies are universal.

'*Can environmental factors or emotional stresses alone produce insanity?*' Most authorities are now inclined to believe that, except in very unusual cases, a person will not become insane *unless* he starts off with some inborn tendency. No more terrible, nerve-racking experiences can be imagined than those which vast numbers of soldiers and civilians underwent during World War II; yet only a relatively small proportion became mentally diseased. Evidence indicates strongly that those who did were especially susceptible. Further, there is considerable evidence that even *chronic alcoholism*, *syphilis*, or other acquired diseases, do not ordinarily result in mental derangement unless there is some predisposition; and that in very old age, while mental faculties may become weaker, actual insanity (*senile dementia*) tends to occur only in those persons who previously had some mental instability. Finally, there is no evidence that anyone can ever 'catch' insanity merely from contact with a mentally diseased person, no matter how close the relationship.

'*How can heredity produce mental disease, or the tendency?*' Since the human brain is a very complex organ, or mechanism, in whose construction and functioning many genes must take part, abnormalities in any of the key genes may upset, derange, or unbalance the mental workings at any given stage of life, especially when there is some severely jarring outside influence. Recent studies suggest that these abnormalities may include particular kinds of chemical or hormonal upsets or deficiencies that directly affect the brain cells and disturb or prevent their orderly workings.

'*If a person inherits "insanity" genes, does this doom him to insanity?*' Not necessarily, and perhaps not at all in many cases. Mental disease need be no different from other diseases, whether inherited or acquired, in the possibilities for prevention and cure. Psychiatrists are making increasing headway in combating threats of mental disease with various means of treatment, among them – most recently – with drugs, such as reserpine and chlorpromazine. This strengthens the theory regarding chemical factors as involved in some of the conditions, and opens the possibility that much more will be done in combating them. Especially important has been the progress in detecting symptoms of mental disease in the early stages, through various behaviour clues and tests, and in some cases through abnormal brain-wave patterns. However, laymen are warned not to make judgements for themselves on the basis of any 'peculiar' behaviour, which may often stem from temporary emotional difficulties rather than any mental disease.

'*How is mental disease different from mental defect?*' There are very important distinctions. 'Mental disease' refers solely to a *derangement* of the mind, without regard to the person's intelligence, which may be of any level up to the highest. 'Mental defect' refers to a *slow-working* or *inferior* mind, which prevents the person's intelligence from going above certain levels. The two conditions are entirely different in their causes and symptoms. Where in some cases a person is both mentally *diseased* and mentally *defective*, it is mostly coincidence. In this chapter we will deal only with mental diseases; in the next chapter with mental defects.

Schizophrenia is the most serious of the common mental diseases, because it starts earliest, is hardest to cure, and accounts for more than half of the persons in mental institutions. The name of the disease comes from two Greek words, *schizo*, meaning 'split', and *phrenia*, mind, and is so called because the afflicted persons tend to have a mind or personality 'split' between the normal and abnormal. The disease is sometimes also called *dementia praecox* (the *praecox* from the Latin for prematurity) because it often appears before or during adolescence, earlier than other common mental diseases. When one reads about demented little children, or high-school boys or girls with mental breakdowns (sometimes leading to suicide or acts of violence), the disease usually is schizophrenia. It first shows itself as a rule by extreme shyness, timidity, not mixing with others, indifference to outside things, etc., accompanied by hysterical periods and other symptoms. There are various types of schizophrenia each with special characteristics: quarrelsomeness and delusions of persecution (*paranoia*); pleasant stupor (*hebephrenia*); violent tantrums, obstinacy or rigidity (*catatonia*). Milder types may show themselves only by occasional freakish or erratic behaviour.

On the basis of many studies, it is believed that schizophrenia is not likely to develop unless there is an inherited predisposition, probably produced through several defective genes – *a pair of recessives*, and perhaps other genes, or other biological factors. This would mean that a child cannot inherit schizophrenia (or the tendency) *from one parent alone*, but must receive one or more of the schizophrenia genes from *each* parent. In the unfortunate cases where couples do have a schizophrenic child, neither parent therefore has the slightest basis for saying, 'It's all because of that insane streak running in *your* family.' Any such inherited tendency in a child would have had to come equally through *both* parents. However, a bad emotional environment in the home, or exposure of the child to special strains, might cause the schizophrenic tendency to develop into the disease itself, and to that extent one parent might be more to blame than the other.

In the general population the average incidence of schizophrenia is about 0·8 per cent, or somewhat under 1 per cent. But wherever close relatives of a person have or had schizophrenia, the threat of developing the disease is very much higher than the average: twenty times the average if a parent was schizophrenic (with the risk rising to an almost two-in-three threat if both parents were so afflicted); fourteen times the average if a brother or sister was schizophrenic; and five times the average if a grandparent, uncle, or aunt had the disease. Among twins, if one of an identical pair is schizophrenic, there is a three-to-one or even four-to-one chance the other will also be or become so, whereas in fraternals the disease occurs in both no more often than in two non-twin children of a family. But the fact that among identical twins one can be schizophrenic and the other not, although carrying the same hereditary factors, shows also how important are environmental influences.

Adding to the belief in the inheritance of the schizophrenic tendency are the increasing numbers of cases of this disease found in very young children, at age two or earlier. Often the disease appears spontaneously, with no evidence of anything wrong in the child's environment. Some psychiatrists believe that babies who are deprived of love and proper attention are most likely to become schizophrenic, but there is strong doubt as to whether any baby will develop the disease unless an inborn tendency was present. Strongly supporting this assumption are findings by Dr Franz Kallmann that children with schizophrenia had schizophrenic relatives in almost the same higher-than-average ratios as were given for afflicted mature persons in the preceding paragraph. In any case, if a schizophrenic child appears, it is grossly unfair to blame the parents without full knowledge of the facts.

Manic-depressive insanity, the second most common mental disease, is so called because those afflicted may swing in periodic moods from mania (highly excitable and sometimes hilarious behaviour) to extreme depression. As the disease progresses it may lead to violent outbursts. But on the whole, manic-depressive insanity is less serious than schizophrenia because (1) it takes less toll in years, most often appearing later in life, during maturity or in middle or old age (although cases are now also being recognized in young children); and (2) it is curable more often and more easily, many manic-depressives recovering after treatment of six months or so (although a dangerous part of the disease is that sometimes individuals who appear cured may suddenly crack up again and commit criminal acts).

There is a strong probability that a tendency to manic-depressive insanity is inherited, but differently and independently from schizophrenia. Although not certain, it is believed that the manic-depressive genes are partly dominant, or irregularly dominant, and that in addition to one or two key genes, certain others, plus some sort of special stresses or environmental influences, must be present. However, the major hereditary difference between this disease and schizophrenia is that in schizophrenia, the predisposition to which is caused mainly by *recessive* genes, inheritance must come equally from *both* parents; but in manic-depressive insanity, since the key genes are at least *partly dominant*, there is a considerably greater threat to a child if only one parent is afflicted. Thus, in schizophrenia, if one parent has the disease, there is an up to one-in-six risk the child will develop it; but in manic-depressive insanity, if one parent is afflicted, the risk may be up to one in three that a child will develop the condition. Also, because the manic-depressive condition usually comes on later in life, it may take a longer time to know if any tendency has been inherited. Finally, the fact that this disease is different in nature and inheritance from schizophrenia has a special significance: if only the one type of mental disease has appeared on one side of a family, and only the other type on the other side, the threat of insanity to offspring is very much less than if the same afflictions had appeared on both sides.

Huntington's chorea is a rare but terrible mental disease, completely unrelated to any of the common types of insanity. Directly inherited through a single dominant gene, it is one of the most dreadful of all human afflictions. For one thing, it strikes at a person in maturity – usually in the thirties or early forties – and from then on causes its victim literally to go to pieces in mind and body, with no known hope of cure, and ending in death after a few years. But the worst feature of Huntington's chorea is that, since it is *dominant* in inheritance and comes on so far along in life, any child of a man or woman with the disease has a one-in-two chance of developing it, but may not know whether he will or will not until almost middle age. Tests now being developed may make it possible to reveal before maturity those who have inherited this dreadful gene, which, if they could then be induced to forego having children of their own, would greatly reduce the chance of the gene's being passed along. As it is, there is the grim fact that more than a thousand of the cases of Huntington's chorea in the United States in the past three centuries had their origin in genes carried by three brothers who came from England in pre-Revolutionary times; and that during the past century, in Minnesota alone, more than a hundred cases of the disease appeared or are on their way to appearing among descendants of one afflicted man born in 1831.

Psychopathic personality is a subtle and often not easily recognized type of mental disease which may cause great suffering, much more to the families of those afflicted and to society at large than to the diseased persons themselves. Psychopaths may often seem to be no more than peculiar persons – rather cold, selfish, and immature – given to lying, deception, and cheating, and to behaviour which under certain conditions may lead to vicious and criminal acts. Fortunately, in other cases psychopaths with brilliant minds and talents may turn their energies into important and useful achievement. The fact that the true psychopath usually gives evidence of his peculiarities in early childhood, and often when there is little or nothing wrong in the environment, leads to the theory that some hereditary quirk is involved. The possibility of some brain disorder as one factor arises from recent reports that a majority of psychopaths have abnormal brain waves.

Neuroses, strictly speaking, are not mental diseases because they include many personality disorders and psychological disturbances found in people who can be classed as fully sane. There is much to indicate that ordinary neurotic behaviour is largely the result of emotional stresses and difficult situations. But it is also not unlikely that heredity predisposes some persons more than others to become neurotic under given conditions. This is suggested by experiments with mice, rabbits, and other lower animals, which show that those of certain breeds are especially prone to develop neuroses when exposed to stresses and conflicts. Also, there is limited recent evidence of psychoneurotic traits (including pathological fears, anxieties, and hysteria) running so strongly in some human families that some investigators think a predisposition to such symptoms may be dominant in inheritance. In any case, since environment, certainly, and heredity, probably, are involved, a fair conclusion is that when parents are definitely of the neurotic type, there is a considerably above average chance that their offspring will become so.

Suicide is often a completely rational (if not justifiable) act. However, perhaps as many as half the suicides in the United States are linked with some kind of mental instability or disease (most often manic-depressive insanity, sometimes schizophrenia – particularly in young people). To the extent, then, that heredity may be involved in the mental condition, it may be playing a part in some suicides and the possible repetitions of the act in some families. At the same time there is much to prove that even if there might be any predisposition to suicide, the act itself is largely dependent on environmental factors. Thus, the suicide rate as a whole in any group, community, or country, or at different times, is directly related to (1) strains which make living less tolerable or bearable (as in depression periods, or during the horror reigns in Europe); (2) the degree of social or religious approval of suicide (the rate being far lower where suicide is strongly condemned, as in Ireland, than where it is sanctioned, as in Japan); and (3) the extent to which in any group individuals are isolated from others and, in periods of distress, can or cannot find help and understanding. Still unexplained, though, is the very high suicide rate among the Scandinavians, who are socially a highly advanced group, and in temperament would appear to be among the world's most stable people.

Another important fact about suicide is that almost everywhere in the world the rate among men is higher than among women – by about four times in the United States, where among whites, sixteen per one thousand males and four per thousand females end their own lives. (Among Negroes the rate is far less – four per one thousand males, one per thousand females.) The chief reason may be that men are under greater pressure to be successful, useful, physically active, and independent, and when they fail in these respects, are more impelled towards suicide. By inheritance, also, as we have seen, males are much more likely to suffer from diseases and defects; and there is some evidence that women inherently have better 'shock absorbers', which can cushion them better against emotional upsets, disasters, and pain. Finally, psychoanalysts might maintain that in so far as self-destruction is aggression turned inward, males, being naturally more aggressive and given to violence than females, would more often commit suicide.

CHAPTER SEVENTEEN

THE MENTAL DEFECTS

WHEN A PERSON'S mind is so slow moving and retarded that he is unable to learn, think, work, and live in a normal way, he is classed as feeble-minded – the general term for all *mental defectives*. (As explained in the preceding chapter, 'mental defect' is entirely different from 'mental disease', or insanity.) Perhaps one in every forty children and adults is in the feeble-minded group. Included are various grades and types of defectives which should not be confused with one another, and which may be due to quite different causes, particularly so far as heredity is concerned.

Technically, the grades of mental defectives are decided by the levels of intelligence they can reach, as measured by their IQ's on various tests (usually the Stanford-Binet). A person is not classed as feeble-minded unless his IQ falls below 70. In turn, the feeble-minded are graded as follows: *morons*, IQ's of 69 down to 50; *imbeciles*, IQ's of 50 down to 20; *idiots*, IQ's of 20 or less. There also are important physical distinctions. The morons as a rule are defective only in intelligence, but with no physical abnormalities, injuries, or diseases to explain their condition. In the idiots and imbeciles, however, defects in bodily functions and physical make-up often go with and may be the cause of the defects in their minds. Moreover, while heredity may play a major part in producing many if not most of the morons, it is much less responsible for the idiots and imbeciles (except some of the rare types). Finally, as we shall see, the risk of having a moron child is closely related to the parents' intelligence (being least for parents with high IQ's, and highest for those of low IQ's), whereas the risk of having an idiot or imbecile child is almost the same for parents of high intelligence as for morons.

The *morons* make up by far the largest proportion – perhaps seven in eight – of the mental defectives. The great majority of morons are physically normal or average, and in only a minority can mental backwardness be traced to environmental causes, such as disease, lack of proper care and training, or learning difficulties unrelated to intelligence. However, in borderline cases mistakes are sometimes made in wrongly grading persons as morons, either because of errors in test scores, or because the tests may fail to measure all phases of intelligence correctly. Thus, a child who may fall down badly on some or many parts of the standard intelligence tests (especially those related to school learning), may be quite average or even above average with respect to certain mental capacities and skills. Many persons rated as morons by their IQ's prove efficient at various jobs, and make good social adjustments.

Where no environmental causes are evident, many authorities believe that morons result mainly from inheritance of 'slow-minded' genes, which keep the brain from functioning beyond a certain degree of efficiency. The best theory is that these genes are *recessive-plus* – a pair of recessives *plus* perhaps a dominant gene or genes. Backing this up are these facts: (1) Moron children are very rare among parents of normal or superior intelligence, and very frequent among parents of low intelligence – more than three fourths of the morons coming from one tenth of the families. (2) If both parents are morons, the chance is anywhere from 60 to 75 per cent that a given child will be, whereas with parents of normal IQ's it may be no more than 1 or 2 per cent, and with parents of above-average IQ's very much less. (3) Once a moron child has been born to two parents, the chance is about one in eight – five times the average – that they will have another retarded child. (4) Among identical twins, if one is a moron, so is the other in almost every case, whereas among fraternal twins this is true in less than half, and perhaps only one fourth of the cases.

Pseudo-feeble-mindedness refers to the infrequent cases of children with normal intelligence who are wrongly classed as morons when parents and teachers are unaware that their backwardness is due to reading difficulties, speech or hearing defects, diseases, or emotional blocks. The mistake is most often made when difficulties of this nature are minor ones and not easily recognized. Careful tests by trained psychologists will easily distinguish the 'pseudo' from the true feeble-minded children, and make possible corrective measures.

Can morons be 'cured'? Reports from time to time of phenomenal improvements or cures of feeble-minded children through this or that treatment must be accepted with extreme caution. In some cases a marked increase in a child's IQ, or mental performance, may follow if he was originally wrongly scored, or if his backwardness was of the 'pseudo' type just discussed. But once it is definitely known that the child's defect centres in a slow brain, the only thing that can be done (so far as science now knows) is to provide training that will make the most of his limited capacities. Much progress in this direction has been reported, but to date none of the much-publicized treatments or 'cures', as with glutamic acid, thiamin, or other chemicals, have been proved effective with morons.

Imbeciles and *idiots*, as previously noted, are defectives with IQ's no higher than 50 – from 50 down to 20 for imbeciles, and below 20 for idiots. Many in both groups also have physical abnormalities or peculiarities usually recognizable at birth, although in some in-between cases the symptoms may not be conclusive until the baby is several years old. The large majority of the imbeciles and idiots result mostly from deficiencies or other unfavourable factors in the prenatal environment, with heredity possibly contributing. (Only in the less common cases is heredity the sole and direct cause.) Despite popular notions, very few cases of idiocy – probably less than one in a hundred – are due to birth injuries, and perhaps no more than another one per cent result from falls on the head or other accidents in infancy and childhood. Among the still-born or miscarried babies who are malformed and defective, it is probable that a considerable percentage would be idiots or imbeciles if they could survive. As it is, the death rates among the low-grade mental defectives both prenatally and in the first years of life is very high, so that those who live to puberty or beyond may represent only a minority.

Mongolian idiots (or imbeciles, depending on the level of intelligence reached) comprise the largest group – about 20 per cent – of all the feeble-minded below the moron level. Out of every thousand babies born, perhaps two or more are 'mongoloids'. The condition gets its name from the peculiar type of eyes, with folds at the corners somewhat as in the Mongolian peoples, which originally led to the mistaken notion that such babies were throwbacks to remote Mongolian ancestors. But there is no racial connexion whatsoever; these idiots may be born to parents of all stocks. Going with the odd eyes are usually a great many other abnormalities: in the nose, forehead, ears, tongue, voice, hands, palm-prints, etc. There may also be organic defects, which cause many mongoloid babies to die in infancy or childhood. If they survive and pass puberty – some of them living well into middle age – they remain stunted in growth and, usually, sexually undeveloped. (Few mongoloids have children.)

The cause of mongolian idiocy, long a mystery, suddenly became clarified in 1958 with the discovery that a chromosome abnormality – an extra one of the chromosomes – was involved. This extra chromosome (one of the small 'autosomes', or non-sex chromosomes), getting into the fertilized egg, in some way disrupts the developmental processes, producing not only defects in the brain, but the other abnormalities noted. Most significantly, this type of chromosome abnormality in eggs is increasingly likely to occur as a woman grows older. Thus, although young mothers, too, sometimes produce mongoloids, almost half are born to mothers over forty. Among mothers under thirty the incidence of mongoloid babies is less than one per thousand; it rises from that age on, sharply as the forties approach, and among mothers over *forty-five*, the rate is one mongoloid baby in every thirty-five to forty births.

Whether there is any hereditary tendency for some mothers more than others to produce the defective types of eggs causing mongolism is uncertain. In any case, it is rare for two mongoloids to be born to the same mother.

Cretinism, another common type of mental defect, arises in an entirely different way from mongolism. In the case of cretinism, the cause, in prenatal life, is a thyroid deficiency in the mother (often if she is goiterous), which stunts the baby's mental and physical development and produces various other abnormalities. In maturity cretins still look like odd little children, with large heads, pot bellies, pug noses, thick lips, and protruding tongues. Cretinism sometimes runs in families, but whether heredity plays any part in this is uncertain. If it does, an unproved theory is that it is by way of recessive genes which either produce some thyroid deficiency in the mother, or some special susceptibility in the child.

Heredity is definitely involved, however, in several other chemically-caused types of mental defect which result not from conditions in the mother but from 'inborn errors of metabolism' in the child – that is, from failures on the part of certain genes to carry through specific chemical processes properly. Among these conditions (all inherited through recessive genes), are *phenylpyruvic idiocy* (or *phenylketonuria*), which shows itself after birth through the excretion of large amounts of phenylpyruvic acid in the urine; *galactosemia*, in which the newborn child lacks a vital enzyme essential for breaking down milk sugar; and *amaurotic family idiocy* (Tay-Sachs disease), in which fatty swellings are produced in the nerve cells of the brain and spinal cord, leading to idiocy, blindness, and paralysis. The latter condition occurs in several types and degrees, the most common bringing death in the early years. *Gargoylism*, another rare inherited chemical disorder, causes idiocy, distorted features, and dwarfism.

It may also be recalled here that mental deficiency often goes with some of the chromosome-caused sex abnormalities, such as the Klinefelter's and Turner's syndromes, discussed in Chapter 13.

Several types of mental defect reveal themselves by abnormally shaped heads. One is *microcephalic idiocy*, in which the individual has an abnormally small head ('pinhead') resulting from an early stoppage in the growth of the brain and the skull. Some cases of microcephaly are inherited through recessive genes, which may lead to several children of this type appearing in one family. But the condition may also be largely or entirely environmental, produced by various prenatal deficiencies or upsets. An occasional cause in recent years has been undue exposure of pregnant mothers to X-rays, a factor likely to increase in menacing importance if there is atomic warfare.

In *hydrocephaly* ('water head') the head is swollen abnormally by fluid in the brain, which often results in mental defect but sometimes does not, especially if there is proper early treatment (including drainage of the fluid). The condition has been found inherited in certain lower animals, and there is a possibility that some (but not all) of the cases in humans may also be hereditary, perhaps through a dominant-qualified gene.

On the whole, most cases of mental deficiency or defectiveness appear due to complex factors – hereditary or environmental, or a combination of both. But whatever the cause, there is increasing hope that in many of the conditions new treatments will be helpful in prevention or in lessening the effects. Even where there is no cure for a specific type of mental defect, better training methods may often enable the retarded individual to be productive and to make some degree of adequate social adjustment.

CHAPTER EIGHTEEN

LENGTH OF LIFE

MANY PEOPLE, past and present, have held to the belief that everyone has an allotted number of years of life. Thus, soldiers say, 'You'll go when your number's up'. This fatalistic view is hardly valid. What is true, however, is that human beings, first as a species – like all other species of animals – and second, as individuals, do have a 'number' set by their heredity for the maximum years that they can live. This number for humans generally, so far as we know now, is greater than for any other living creatures, except the giant tortoises and turtles, which may live to ages of 180 or more.

The Bible speaks of humans who lived to much longer 'years' (Adam, 930, Methuselah, 969, Cainan, 910, etc.), but authorities believe these pre-Flood Biblical 'years' may have referred to periods little more than a tenth of our modern years. Also it is believed that the ages of post-Flood Biblical personages (Abraham, 175, Isaac, 180, etc.) were computed by systems different from those by which we reckon years today. It is significant that at a later stage the Bible referred to man's allotted years as 'three score and ten' (70), which – by coincidence or not – is almost exactly the average expectation of life in the United States today.

As in the past, reports continue to appear from time to time of persons supposedly living to the age of 130, 140, 150, etc. Almost invariably these persons are from remote backward regions or countries, with no authentic records to support their claims. Actually, proved human longevity records of modern times do not go beyond the age of 116 or so. Moreover, despite the fact that we are living in the most favourable period for longevity in the world's history, only about four or five persons in 100,000 are reaching or passing the age of one hundred.

Taking present life spans in the United States from birth to death, people as a whole are now living almost a third longer than they did at the beginning of the century, and almost twice as long as in George Washington's time (the end of the eighteenth century) – that is if we compare the present life expectancy at birth of almost seventy years, with the average expectancy in 1900 of forty-eight years, and at the time of the American Revolution of about thirty-five. This tremendous gain has obviously not been because of any change in heredity, but solely because of the enormous improvement in health, living conditions, and medical care. Mainly this has brought greatly reduced death rates in infancy, childhood, and early maturity, enabling many more persons to live into the older ages. For people past middle life, however, the longevity chances are only a few years better than a half century ago, and for those reaching seventy, only about a year better, showing that despite environmental improvements, a general longevity time limit is still at work on human life spans.

Whatever the average longevity limits for humans may be, there is little doubt but that some individuals are geared by their hereditary make-up for longer 'runs' or life spans than are others, given equal environmental conditions. Some of the ways in which 'longevity' genes may work or be kept from working have been suggested in the chapters on diseases and defects. In certain conditions there are 'killer' genes (technically called *lethals*) which bring death almost before a life is under way; in other hereditary conditions death may be set to occur at various more or less definite periods, in childhood, at puberty, in early maturity, or before middle age. Less directly, there are various hereditary defects or weaknesses affecting the heart and arteries, kidneys, and other vital organs, the nervous system, body tissues, etc., which may decrease individuals' survival chances. Predispositions to mental disease may also curtail longevity chances by adversely affecting the person's way of living, or inducing suicide. Finally, different gene combinations undoubtedly tend to construct the bodies and influence the general functioning of individuals in different ways, all of which have a bearing on the rates of wear and tear, disease resistance, ageing, and risks of vital breakdowns. Thus, in so far as their genes may differ, no two individuals start out with exactly the same longevity chances. But the best of heredity can only give a person the possibility of living until such and such an age if the conditions are right. A sudden accident can cancel out all the effects of 'long-life' genes.

Some clues as to the relative importance of heredity and environment on life spans are offered by the twin studies of Dr Franz Kallmann and others. Findings are that identical twins are much closer in their ages lived and in the symptoms of ageing than are fraternals. However, while the matching hereditary factors of identicals may contribute towards making their life spans much the same, similar environments also are involved. By the same token, differences in environment can can cause one identical to much outlive the other, starting with the fact that sometimes one identical dies at birth while the other lives to a ripe old age, despite their having the same 'longevity' genes.

As we have seen, we may make some guesses about a person's 'longevity' genes by knowing what hereditary defects he may or may not have. But also important may be the longevity records of his parents, grandparents, and other near relatives, because various studies have indicated that tendencies to longer or shorter life spans run in families under the same outside conditions. Mostly the differences are related to the incidences of death from major diseases. For instance, a recent study by life-insurance companies shows that persons two or more members of whose immediate family died from heart and related conditions under age sixty, had about a 40 per cent higher than average death risk for their age. Family histories of diabetes, cancer, mental disease, and other conditions also may affect individuals' longevity chances, unless it is clear that they themselves are free of the conditions.

In general, persons both of whose parents were long-lived stand a better chance of reaching a ripe old age than do those with only one long-lived parent, and a much better chance than those with two short-lived parents. In every case, however, one must establish the causes of the parents' deaths: if due only to accident, infectious diseases, or other purely environmental factors, their children's own longevity chances need obviously not be affected (unless they also were exposed to the same bad environmental factors). At the same time, even if hereditary conditions played a part in the parents' deaths, many such conditions may now (or presently) be checked, restrained, or cured by treatment. In either case, a family history of short life need not at all mean that any given member may not be long-lived.

By far the most important general influence on any person's longevity chances is his or her sex. We have seen in earlier chapters how heredity works to make males much more likely than females to develop a great many diseases and defects which are sex-linked (with genes on the X chromosome), and also more vulnerable to many serious conditions which are not directly hereditary, but in which heredity may play a part, or to which the male system is particularly susceptible. This applies to virtually all major death-producing conditions except diabetes, exophthalmic goitre, and gallstones, and, of course, the specifically female cancers. There also seem to be certain general factors in the female systems which enable them to stand up better under environmental hazards of many kinds – accidents, shocks, infections, starvation, etc.

Thus, as brought out in Chapter 11, long before there are any environmental differences for the two sexes, in prenatal life and in infancy, the male death rate is about 30 per cent higher. (It is worth noting that among almost all lower animals there is also an excess of male deaths in early life.) In childhood and youth there is a drop of 12 per cent more male than female deaths, but in maturity the male death rate climbs again to a 30 per cent margin over that of females. However, after early childhood a considerable part (though far from all) of the excess male death rate is caused by the male's greater exposure to accidents, war, occupational diseases and various other adverse factors. Throwing the longevity balance further towards females is the fact that improvements in environment, medical care, and social conditions have benefited them relatively more than males. For one thing, deaths through childbearing have been cut to a small fraction of what they once were (now less than one in two thousand births in the United States – or one twelfth the rate in 1915).

The foregoing facts show up clearly in the present estimates of years remaining for men and women of different ages. At birth today the life expectation for an American male is just over 66, for a female, over 72. In maturity and through middle life the male's further life expectancy at every age is from five to four years less than the female's. The margin declines with the older ages, but always continues in favour of women. While these figures are for persons in the United States, they apply closely to those in other advanced countries as well. However, in less favoured countries where poor environments bring high death rates, particularly in childbearing, women have almost as low life expectancies as men.

All of the foregoing facts have an important bearing on the relative numbers of males and females in any population, and on the resulting social consequences. As we saw in Chapter 4, the sexes start off at birth with about 106 boys born to every 100 girls. From then on the higher death rate of males steadily reduces their excess numbers, so that in early maturity the male excess is virtually wiped out, and by middle life there are about 15 per cent more women. In the seventies there are 20 per cent more women, and from about ninety on, almost twice as many women as men surviving. These figures are for the United States. The excess of women at the different ages is even greater in England, Germany, and France. But as stated before, in less advanced countries, where environments are bad, the excess of women is much less.

With respect to group difference in longevity, many mistakes were formerly made in comparing long-lived and short-lived stocks, races, groups, or classes of human beings, and ascribing their differences to superior or inferior hereditary make-up. As we have seen, heredity does tend to make many individuals and families longer lived than others, but this can be proved only when all the persons involved live under the same conditions. It is another matter when the environments differ greatly, for it may then be not the hereditary, but the environmental factors which account for the differences in longevity. Thus, one finds today (as there has always been) a fairly close relationship between longevity averages and the conditions existing among different groups in the same city, state, or country, whatever their race or ethnic stock.

While racial groups may differ to some extent in their inherited susceptibility to various diseases and defects, there is no evidence that when all factors are taken together, people of any race are destined by heredity to outlive others. There is much to indicate that such racial longevity differences as there are, may be due mainly to environment. For instance, Negro life expectancies in the United States in 1900 were almost sixteen years less than those of whites. But as conditions for Negroes improved, so did their life expectancies, until today their average longevity is only about six years less than that of whites, and might eventually become the same. Already one may note that present Negro life expectancies are much higher than those of many white groups in other parts of the world today, or than the life expectancies of American whites a half century ago.

Among European whites, and among foreign-born Americans and their children, those of different stocks show differences both in longevity and in death rates from specific causes. For example, Irish-Americans have a considerably higher death rate than Italian-Americans, and there also are differences in their causes of death. In turn, other longevity and death-rate differences appear among Americans of English, Russian, Polish, German, Jewish, and other ethnic origins. But since these groups differ from each other in living habits, diets, and occupations, it is difficult to tell whether their longevity differences are due solely to environmental factors or whether (as some authorities believe) heredity also plays a part.

Husband-Wife Survival

(Based on current life expectancies in the United States)

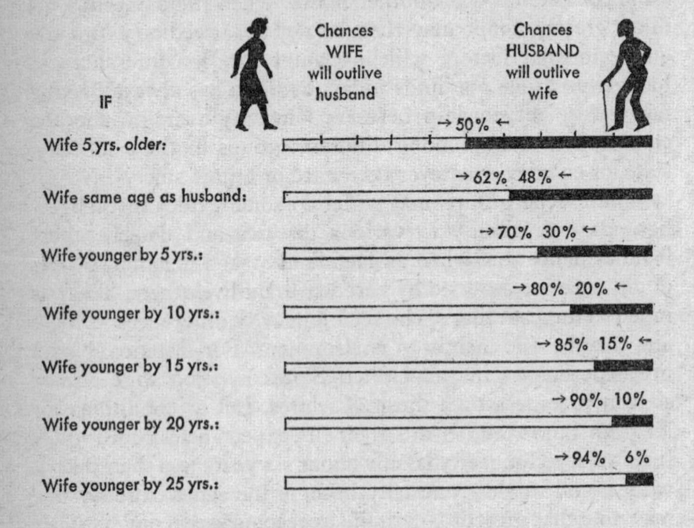

Statistics compiled by Metropolitan Life Insurance Company.

Equivalent British Figures

Age inteval	*Chance that wife will outlive husband*
Wife 5 years older	49%
Same age	61%
Wife 5 years younger	73%
,, 10 ,, ,,	81%
,, 15 ,, ,,	88%
,, 20 ,, ,,	92%
,, 25 ,,	94%

Within all groups – as classified by sex, family, race, ethnic origin, or living standards – the longevity chances for given individuals have been found related to the following factors in which hereditary tendencies may be involved:

Personal health. The chief influences on one's longevity chances are the absence or presence of the major degenerative diseases – heart and artery, kidney and lung diseases, diabetes, cancer, etc. Apart from these and some of the less common conditions known to be fatal, one may be a chronic invalid and yet live a long life.

Body build. One's weight has considerable bearing on life-expectancy because it worsens the threats from many diseases. Persons who are 25 per cent or more overweight for their age have a death rate about 75 per cent higher than those of average weight. Extreme underweight in young people also is a threat to life-expectancy, but perhaps only because it often is a symptom of some disease or internal disorder. Among older people leanness may be an asset for longevity. Moderately tall persons also have better than average longevity chances – probably because those in the more favoured groups tend to be above average in height. But extreme tallness (well over seven feet) is often a symptom of a glandular disorder, and may carry the threat of a shortened life span.

Blood pressure and pulse. The higher one's blood pressure, the shorter the life expectancy, as a rule, because of the association with heart–arterial–kidney diseases. Low blood pressure (if not extremely low) may be a longevity asset. Too rapid pulse (near or over 100 per minute) or very irregular pulse, may also decrease longevity chances, particularly if there is overweight or hypertension. Heart murmurs of certain types (functional – 'inconstant apical', or 'systolic pulmonic') are quite harmless, but other types of heart murmurs (organic), are symptomatic of various heart diseases, which are possible life-shorteners.

Occupation. The more one's job affords opportunities for healthy and careful living, the better the longevity chances, from extra months to extra years. As groups, the longest-lived are professional people – clergymen, teachers, lawyers, and engineers, with doctors having somewhat shorter life-expectancies. Next in longevity are business executives, white-collar workers, skilled workers. Writers, artists, and musicians as a group have somewhat shorter than average life spans. Shortest-lived are unskilled workers, miners, quarrymen, and others exposed to irritating dusts and other disease hazards; itinerant workers characterized by hard-living, careless habits; and men in various dangerous occupations. Farmers are hard to classify because they are of different levels, their life-expectancies going with their living conditions, but in general they are among the longest-lived persons either because their work is more healthful, or because they have to be healthy to be farmers.

Temperaments and habits. Persons who are excitable and fast-living do not as a rule live as long as the placid and easygoing ones, and in this heredity may play some part. (In lower animals, too, the most active species and breeds, which burn up the most energy, tend to be the shorter-lived.) Excessive smoking and drinking, to the extent that they go with tenseness and instability (hereditary or otherwise), may also be life-shorteners. But in some individuals moderate drinking and/or moderate smoking may be relaxing and not detrimental to longevity.

How much farther longevity of human beings can be extended is highly uncertain. Apart from the general improvements in environment and medical care, no life-prolonging or rejuvenating methods have yet proved to be successful. This applies to hormone treatments, rejuvenating 'serums', diets, or foods of one kind or another. Perhaps the average longevity may in a generation or two reach seventy-five for women and seventy for men. But whether it can go much beyond that, or whether any human individuals can be enabled to live to ages of 120 or over, depends entirely on what limits have been set by human heredity. These limits are still anyone's guess.

CHAPTER NINETEEN

INTELLIGENCE

IF HEREDITY PRODUCES different degrees of abnormal and low intelligence, should it not also produce different degrees of *normal* and *superior* intelligence? Undoubtedly it does, for variations in intelligence are no less subject to the workings of genes than are variations in size or stature, or in physical functions. We see this most clearly in comparing the mental capacities of human beings and of lower animals, and often, the responses of various breeds within a given species, such as dogs. There can be no argument that these differences are overwhelmingly due to heredity. What is at issue is only whether – or to what extent – the relatively small differences in normal intelligence among human beings themselves are also produced by heredity. This, as we shall see, is extremely hard to establish, because human intelligence is far more complex than it was formerly thought to be, and is so greatly subject to environmental influences. Nevertheless, even the limited evidence available is sufficient to refute many wrong beliefs about human minds and to make clear how heredity and environment interact to influence them.

In everyday life we rate people as 'brilliant', 'bright', 'ordinary', 'stupid', etc. But even if these offhand ratings are correct, psychologists are well aware that the intelligence *shown* by an individual does not necessarily reflect the true quality of his mind. Many persons never had or have the chance to develop their mental capacities fully, and are frequently misjudged because of the common tendency to confuse intelligence with *education*. Thus, before we can tell what role heredity plays in human mentality, we must have scientific standards for measuring it.

There is increasing awareness that intelligence is not a single trait, as was formerly thought, but a combination of a great many traits and capacities. Among them are abstract thinking, quickness of learning, memory, word fluency, language comprehension, arithmetical ability, speed of judgement, ability to visualize shapes and spaces, ability to 'sense' people, 'intuition', etc. The different elements of intelligence may not go together in the same persons, which helps to explain why some are bright or capable in certain ways and not in others.

Since intelligence is compounded of many capacities, a great many genes undoubtedly contribute to its quality and type. Most probably there are, first, a large number of genes, in different orders of importance, which govern the general construction of the brain and brain cells, their functioning and their 'hook-ups' with the sensory organs and other parts of the nervous system. Second, there are additional genes involved in particular processes relating to specific mental traits and abilities. But this must remain theoretical until these 'mental' genes are identified and their effects determined.

The various widely used intelligence tests are extremely helpful in measuring the relative mental *performances* of individuals. But how far the tests also dig beneath environmental influences and measure inborn mental *capacities* is a question. Actually, the standard tests (such as the Stanford-Binet) measure mainly the academic abilities required for mastering the usual school subjects. Other tests also help to measure special abilities needed for given tasks, jobs, and professions. Where the tests so far are weakest is in measurement of (1) 'social intelligence', involved in understanding other people and getting along with them; (2) traits such as 'drive', curiosity, sense of humour, shrewdness, or 'intuition'; and (3) unusual qualities of the mind involved in 'creativeness', 'originality', or mechanical ability, needed in many fields.

IQ scores are derived through two kinds of tests, one for children, one for adults. The IQ's of children, up to age sixteen, are determined by how well or poorly a child does in comparison with the average for his age. In Chapter 17 there were given the subnormal IQ ratings under 70, for idiots, imbeciles, and morons. IQ's of 70 to 80 are in the 'borderline' group. Beyond these, individuals are classified by IQ's as follows: 80 to 90, 'dull–normal'; 90 to 110, 'normal'; 110–120, 'superior'; 120–140, 'very superior'; 140 or over, 'genius' (only in the technical 'IQ' sense, but not as applied to the true and extremely rare geniuses to be dealt with in Chapter 20).

Psychologists have long gone on the assumption that intelligence becomes 'set' towards the end of adolescence. For this reason, the intelligence tests for persons of all ages after sixteen made little allowance for age. Any advantages of younger adults on some parts of the tests, because of quicker minds and better memory, were considered offset on other parts of the tests by older persons' greater store of acquired knowledge and experience. But as with children's IQ's, there is still much uncertainty as to how closely adult test scores reflect basic or all-round intelligence.

The same person's IQ may sometimes be given as different by several points (up to 10 or more) on tests in successive years, or even within a few weeks or months. This may be because of differences in the tests or test methods, or in the examiners, or in the person's state of health, energy, and degrees of application. In very young normal children (under five), IQ's are not too easily or reliably determined. (Unrecognized reading or hearing difficulties, emotional and psychological blocks, and sometimes physical factors, may occasionally impede a young child's mental performance, or cause it to vary greatly from one year to another.) But at older ages an individual's IQ ordinarily tends to remain fairly constant from year to year.

To the extent that IQ's are not always true measures of mental capacities, they may also not be accurate forecasts of future success or failure. Nevertheless, IQ's are becoming more and more important in determining how children will be educated, and which students will be admitted to the more selective colleges and accepted for medical and other professional schools. IQ's and other test scores also are being used in engaging workers for various jobs in industries, and by the armed forces in choosing men for special training and advancement. Thus, IQ's and the opportunities for achievement, if not achievement itself, are becoming more closely related. As one example, the large group of high IQ (150 average) individuals who as children began to be studied by Professor Lewis M. Terman in 1921, and who have been followed up since, have for the most part continued to be outstanding both in IQ's and in achievements. On the other hand, to prove that a high IQ alone does not insure success, a number of persons in this group failed in college and ended up in lowly jobs.

What of the *inheritance* of intelligence? Studies on this point so far depend mainly on comparisons of the IQ's of parents and children, and of identical and fraternal twins in relation to non-twin brothers and sisters. Taking up the first relationship, there is much evidence that IQ's of children, on the average, are fairly close to those of their parents. In individual instances this may not be so, but taking families collectively, parents with high IQ's tend to have children of well-above-average brightness and, rarely, a dull child (except for the defective cases discussed in Chapter 17). In the opposite direction, parents with low IQ's, as a group, tend to have low-IQ children and only very rarely a brilliant child. (See also concluding section of this chapter.)

Supporting what has been said, various studies show that IQ's of children of men engaged in the 'brainier' jobs tend to be higher than those of men in jobs requiring less mental ability. Thus, children of professional men have IQ's averaging 116; of semi-professional men and business executives, 112; of upper white-collar men, most businessmen, and skilled workers, 104; of slightly skilled workers, 97; of day labourers, 96. (Figures for the United States, but closely paralleled in England and other countries, including the Soviet Union.)

How far the facts presented prove inheritance of intelligence depends on the fairness of the tests for the different groups. There is some evidence that the IQ tests may indeed be slanted towards the kind of learning acquired by children from the more educated and more privileged homes. Therefore these children would tend to score higher IQ's than less privileged children, even if hereditary factors were equal. Yet it cannot be ignored that the mental environments provided for children are in themselves considerably influenced by how basically intelligent or unintelligent their parents are. Allowing for all biases, then, the relationships between parents' and children's IQ's very likely reflect the influence of both heredity and environment.

Added proof of the role of heredity in intelligence is seen in findings that the IQ differences between identical (one-egg) twins are quite small (5·9 points), and even when *reared apart* average 7·7 points, whereas the IQ differences between fraternal (two-egg) twins *reared together* average 8·4 points, and between non-twin siblings (brothers or sisters) reared together, 14·5 points. However, about one in twenty identical twins (including some reared together) differ in IQ by 15 points or more, indicating how much environment can affect intelligence-test scores. Of further interest are studies made in orphanages some years ago which showed a much closer relationship between the IQ's of brothers and/or sisters in the same institution than between unrelated children, even though all were in the same environments, and regardless of how long they'd been there.

There is uncertainty, however, as to the degree to which the IQ's of adopted children tend to follow those of their true parents or of their foster parents. Conflicting findings are due to special difficulties in making this type of study. One can hardly doubt that an adopted child's IQ will be influenced by the care, training, and education he or she receives. But perhaps the majority of experts would hold that if two adopted children were reared in the same home in the same way, a child whose true parents were mentally superior would be considerably more likely to show high intelligence than would a child whose true parents were mentally only average, or below average.

Among normal individuals in general, there is little indication that the mental genes are linked with genes for physical traits, or that under ordinary circumstances the bodily condition affects the IQ by more than a few points either way. Although present-day children are on the average much healthier, and taller for their ages, than were children of previous generations (and, often, than their parents were), few would maintain that they are notably brighter. Nor have persons in Europe today who as children during World War II suffered the most extreme hardships and the scantiest diets, turned out to be any less intelligent than those reared under the best conditions elsewhere. Going far back, the cave men of fifty thousand years ago, scientists believe, had as much brain power as modern human beings, despite enormous differences in health, diet, and physical make-up.

Again, popular notions that the size of the head, forehead, or brain offers a good clue to a person's intelligence, have little scientific support. As between lower animals and human beings the very great differences in brain size and structure (particularly in the forepart, the *cerebral cortex*) do go with their relative mental capacities. But among human beings themselves the sizes of brains (other than in abnormal cases, such as of microcephalic, or 'pinhead', idiots) are of little significance as compared with their qualitative structure and functioning. Whites, for instance, have smaller brains on the average than Eskimos; some geniuses have had big heads, some small heads; and many prehistoric men had bigger brains than modern men. As it is, no brain specialist can yet tell from the size, shape, or convolutions of a normal brain how intelligent an individual might be or was.

Where bodily factors working in a highly complex way may possibly affect intelligence in the *direction* it takes, if not its *quantity*, is in the sexes. Within any group, anywhere, one can find important differences in mental qualities and performances between boys and girls, men and women. But since the environments, rearing, objectives, and roles of the two sexes are not and never can be completely the same, one cannot expect to measure accurately their mental capacities on the same scale or to prove that either sex is superior, inferior, or even precisely equal in total intelligence to the other. Only in their performances on specific mental tasks can the sexes be properly compared. Here are some findings:

Girls from the earliest ages are consistently better in finger dexterity (lacing shoes, dressing themselves, etc.); in tests involving language (little girls begin to talk earlier than do boys, as a rule, and many fewer girls have speech difficulties); reading and writing; memory (of songs, and of what they've read); aesthetic responses (matching shapes and colours); and 'sensing' people and noting details about them. In high school and college, girls continue to be superior in verbal tests and modern foreign languages (but not Latin).

Boys are consistently superior as a group in abstract reasoning, mathematics, mechanical ability, structural skills and curiosity about the way things are put together, or what is happening outside them. As they go on into college, boys excel in the sciences, mathematics, history, civics, and economics. Also, in groups starting out with the same high IQ's or scholarship levels, more boys remain at the high level, more girls drop behind.

What causes these sex differences? Recent studies throw doubt on previous theories that all the sex differences in mental performance are due to 'social conditioning'. As we saw in previous discussions of sex differences, the XX and XY chromosome mechanisms set off the development of numerous differences between the sexes in biological make-up and functioning. There is every reason why inborn sex differences would also influence the mental processes, but how or to what extent they do so awaits proof. One fact should not be overlooked: as education and training of women has more closely approached that of men, and their opportunities for jobs and service have been extended, they have shown capacities in many fields for which their 'minds' were previously thought unfitted.

Race differences in intelligence also must be analysed very carefully before drawing conclusions. Whatever differences might currently be found in the thinking and mental achievements of persons of different races and nationalities, there is no way yet of proving that these are inborn. The chief problem, as already indicated, is that the available intelligence tests cannot be fairly and equally applied to groups of people reared, educated, and living under markedly different conditions. Further, since the standard tests were mainly devised by and for white Europeans and Americans, they may discriminate against individuals of other races and nationalities.

The foregoing observations apply particularly to any findings that average IQ's of Negroes are below those of whites. An unquestioned fact is that environments and learning opportunities of Negroes have for generations been inferior to those of whites and, despite great advances in recent years, still are. Wherever Negroes enjoy relatively more equality and more opportunity for education, their IQ's average considerably higher than in areas where they are repressed. In fact, among American Army draftees in World War II, Negroes from some Northern states had considerably lower rejection rates for substandard intelligence than had whites from some Southern states. There also has been a marked increase in the relative numbers of Negro children with high IQ's (140 to 150 or over), and in Negro individuals reaching to professional ranks. Most authorities feel that until environments are fully equalized, no valid conclusions can be drawn about the relative IQ's or mental capacities of white and Negroes, or those of other races.

Thus, despite the uncertainties dealt with in this chapter, these conclusions are justified:

– The intelligence any person *shows* is always the combined result of his heredity and his environment.

– *Physical* influences (health, diet, climate, comforts, etc.) are less likely to affect a person's mental performance than are *psychological* influences and opportunities for learning.

– The inherited mental factors are so numerous, of so many kinds, work in such complex ways, and are so difficult to determine and measure, that no precise predictions can be made about the transmission of intelligence from parents to children according to any such ratios or formulas as are possible with respect to many simpler traits.

What can only be said is that high intelligence, judged by *both* high IQ and achievement, signifies the presence of superior mental genes. If both parents are of this type, the children are more likely to start off with superior mental equipment than if only one parent shows high intelligence, and much more so than if neither parent is mentally outstanding. However, where parents are exceptionally brilliant, the odds are that the children will not quite approach their mental levels. On the other hand, parents of below-average IQ's may well have children with IQ's averaging considerably higher than theirs, particularly if the parents had lacked opportunities for adequate mental development.

It may never be possible to draw conclusions about the inheritance of a person's *whole* intelligence. But it may eventually be quite possible to measure and predict the inheritance of separate elements of intelligence, or of different mental abilities and capacities, each of which may be influenced by different genes.

CHAPTER TWENTY

TALENT AND GENIUS

MOST PEOPLE find out in the course of time that they are good at certain things and not at others. Alert parents will notice children showing special talents at early ages and will also be aware that one child may differ markedly from another in given abilities. What causes these differences? A first important fact is that special aptitudes or talents need not be related to intelligence. A person may be good at music, painting, writing, knitting, pie-baking or what not, and yet be much less bright than someone who is a bungler at the same speciality. Again, different abilities may or may not be related to one another. Some persons are good at many things, others seem to be good at only one thing. And for any given ability, there may be a range from up to 'phenomenal' down to nearly zero. All this would suggest that just as there are genes that govern a person's capacity to develop physically and mentally in various ways, there may be genes that govern or influence his capacity to develop special abilities. However, we are just beginning to identify particular 'talent' genes and to evolve theories as to how they work – always keeping in mind that the expression of any talent can be much influenced by environment.

Of all human talents, *musical talent* gives the clearest evidence of heredity because it reveals itself most spontaneously, at the earliest ages, and in all sorts of environments, and because there is abundant evidence that it runs brilliantly in particular families. Further, in musical *performance*, the talent of one individual can be much more easily compared with that of another than is the case in other arts and fields of achievement. (Many of the facts that follow are derived from the author's own study of the talent backgrounds of large groups of outstanding musical virtuosi and opera singers.

The study is reported in detail in the author's book *You and Heredity*.)

In almost every case great musical talent expresses itself before the age of five or six, and often as early as age two or three. It may appear without any training, being revealed through singing, humming, or response to music, sometimes in a baby who has not yet learned to talk. Many authorities believe that if marked musical ability is not definitely revealed, or cannot be detected, in the very early years, there is little likelihood that it will be developed later.

Usually, also, there is marked talent in parents and/or near-relatives of great musicians. But as proof that a musical home is not of itself the determining factor, some of the greatest virtuosi came from untalented families, and many brilliant musicians have found regretfully that their children, despite the finest musical environment, failed to develop talent.

As a basis for musical talent, there must be superiority in the musical aptitudes – the senses of pitch, time, intensity (loudness and softness), harmony, rhythm, and musical memory (which can be measured by current standard tests – Seashore, Thorpe-Whistler, Drake, etc.). Degrees of capacity with respect to each of these senses *separately*, and not as a group, appear to be inborn: first, because one sense may be present without the other, so that a person can have a keen sense of time, but not of harmony, or may have a fine sense of rhythm and harmony, but poor musical memory, etc. Second, training cannot be shown to 'create' any of these senses, or (say authorities) to improve them much beyond the degree that the inborn capacity for development is there. All this would suggest that there are separate genes for each musical sense, working with different degrees of intensity.

Absolute pitch – the ability to 'hit' or judge any note correctly by ear alone – gives evidence of being inborn. While it is found in many virtuosi and is usually revealed in childhood, the great majority of outstanding musicians fail to develop it despite years of practice. On the other hand, many persons without musical training have absolute pitch from the start, and many have it with little else in the way of musical aptitude. Strengthening belief of its inheritance (possibly through a dominant gene) is the fact that absolute pitch may run in families for successive generations, as for example in the singer Kirsten Flagstad, her mother, maternal grandmother, and maternal granduncle.

Tune deafness or *tone deafness* – the inability to carry a tune, or to recognize tunes, which afflicts some individuals – is believed due to heredity in many, if not most, cases. In families where it appears there is evidence that the condition may be caused by a dominant gene. If true, such a gene could completely block the appearance of musical aptitude or musical development, regardless of how superior the afflicted person's other musical genes might be.

As to *musicians' hands* music experts belittle the popular notion that particular shapes of hands or fingers destine a child to become a good musician, and failure to have them means that he won't be. While some hands are unquestionably better constructed than others for developing performing technique, varied types of hands and fingers are found among top musicians, and some have anything but 'long, tapering fingers'. Any special 'sensitivity' in musicians' hands is mostly the result of the way they've been used.

How, then, can musicial virtuosity be inherited? A good assumption is that although a great many genes contribute to musical talent, the majority are in wide circulation; anyone who can carry a tune or learn to play a musical instrument must have many of them. But the special key genes required for great talent are rare. However, the fact that great musical talent can persist through three or four generations would indicate that these key genes are limited in number, and are probably dominant, since otherwise the needed combination could not long be maintained.

Let us suppose that there are five of the superior or 'virtuoso' key genes for the basic musical senses, which we will designate in this way: M*U*S*I*C*. Next, the ordinary genes for the same senses could be designated in this way (without the stars): M–U–S–I–C. Finally, representing the inferior or defective genes (with small letters: m–u–s–i–c. Since each person receives a pair of genes of every type – one gene from each parent – any combination of superior, ordinary, and inferior 'talent' genes could be inherited: (M*U–Uu–S*S–I*i–CC), or (Mm–U*U–S*s–II–C*C) or (mm–uu–Ss–II–Cc*), etc., producing talent or aptitude in various degrees. Only with at least one virtuoso (starred) gene *of each type* in every pair would great talent result: (M*M–U*U–S*S–I*I–C*C). This could explain a number of hitherto puzzling situations.

Untalented parents, talented child. If each parent carried only part of the needed gene combination, neither parent alone would show much talent. But between them they could contribute all the genes required to produce a highly talented (M*U*S*I*C*) child.

Talented parents, untalented children. Even the most musically talented persons are undoubtedly carrying – in addition to their superior genes – some 'hidden' genes which are ordinary and possibly inferior, so it is quite likely that the new gene combination received by any child will not be as talent-producing as that of the parent. This would be particularly so if the other parent was not talented.

Talented parents, talented children. Although an untalented child may also appear, as explained above, the more talent there is in both parents, the greater is the chance that a child will receive the needed 'talent-gene' combination. Thus, the author's study of virtuosi musicians and singers showed that where both their parents were talented, there was also talent in about 70 per cent of their brothers and sisters; where one parent was talented, in about 60 per cent; where neither parent was talented, in only 15 per cent.

But a great deal more than musical aptitude is required if the musician is to reach the heights in his field. Also essential are such qualities as feeling, sensitivity, powers of concentration, drive and stamina, plus 'personality'. How much heredity may contribute to these qualities is still unknown. At any rate, deficiencies in these traits, as well as unfavourable turns in the environment, may help to explain why so many musical prodigies peter out in later years.

Composing talent is in a special category. While the highest degree of musicality is required for the great composer, as for the great musical performer, the special talents needed for one do not necessarily go with those for the other. Many great composers have been undistinguished performers, and many virtuosi musicians have shown no talent for composition. Whatever the special composing gifts may be, they also appear to have a hereditary basis and to reveal themselves through precociousness and spontaneity. Thus Handel was composing church services at eleven; Mozart at fourteen had a score of symphonies and short operas to his credit; and Mendelssohn and Schubert by age seventeen or eighteen were already notable composers. More specific knowledge regarding the role played by heredity in composing talent is lacking mainly because there are as yet no reliable tests for identifying and measuring its basic elements. This is true of all the arts involving 'creativity', as we shall explain later.

Why have there been no women among great composers? This is one of the great mysteries. Many woman have shown outstanding talent as musicians, and some have been recognized as among the most gifted composers of songs and études. But no woman has ever been credited with producing a great symphony, or other musical work of the highest type. Possible reasons for this will be discussed towards the end of this chapter.

One more point: virtually all of the musical-talent studies to date have been of musicians in the 'classical' field. But there is every possibility that most of the general facts brought out here also apply to outstanding composers and performers of semi-classical and popular music.

Coming now to *vocal talent*, a common mistake is to suppose that to be a great singer, one need only be born with a great voice. But the voice is only an instrument – like the pianist's piano or the violinist's violin. To be an outstanding singer also requires great musical talent, so that the vocal equipment can be developed and used properly. Thus, much of what has been said about the inheritance of musical talent in instrumentalists also applies to singers. The important differences stem from the fact that the singer's instrument is part of himself and that he is at all times at the mercy of its condition. Also, because the permanent quality of the voice cannot be determined until puberty, intensive vocal training usually doesn't begin until then or later. Finally, such external factors as the singer's looks, personality, and dramatic ability, plus the whims of the public, play a much greater role in the vocal than in the instrumental fields. Nevertheless, the records of the great singers all point to a high degree of inborn musicality, and their family backgrounds reveal almost as much talent as do those of the virtuosi musicians.

Voice types also may be inherited. Limited evidence indicates that *bass* voices in men and *soprano* voices in women are determined by one type of voice genes; that a different type of gene produces *tenor* in men, *alto* in women; and that a mixed pair of genes – one of each type – produces *baritone* in men, *mezzo-soprano* in women. The author's own study further suggests that where both parents have high voices (father, tenor; mother, soprano) the children's voices will tend to produce a marked majority of low-voiced sons. Among European whites, the highest incidence of bassos and sopranos, 61 per cent, is in north-west Germany, the lowest, 12 per cent, in Sicily.

Taking together now all forms of musicality, it would appear that people of some races or nationalities undoubtedly *show* more talent for music, or for particular forms of musical expression, than do others. One must be struck by the preponderance of Italian opera composers, conductors, and singers; of Jewish violinists, pianists, and composers of both classical and popular music; of Negroes among jazz musicians, composers, and singers; and of the special musical characteristics of various other racial or ethnic groups. Most authorities feel that these can be explained by differences not in heredity, but in musical atmosphere and environment. For example, the psychological environment of Negroes may explain why they express themselves in 'blues', in particular types of rhythm, and in their special folk songs and 'spirituals'; at the same time with limited chance for training in classical music, their musicians and singers have turned largely to the popular fields. Tests so far made of the basic musical senses of rhythm, time, harmony, etc., have shown no significant differences between Negro and white children, nor of these as compared with other racial and ethnic groups. However, geneticists believe we cannot entirely dismiss the possibility that special types of 'music-talent' genes might be distributed differently, to some extent at least, among the peoples of the world. For the time being, it is well to conclude that musical talent is found plentifully among all peoples, and that the degree to which it has expressed itself so far has been largely dependent upon opportunity and training.

The talent for music is undoubtedly not alone in requiring special hereditary capacities. Particular inborn endowments may be equally necessary for high achievement in painting, sculpture, writing, acting, dancing, and other arts, as well as in science and invention. But in these other fields any inherited factors are harder to identify because of the greater and more complex role played by environment.

The term *born artist* is often rather loosely applied to anyone having characteristics supposed to go with persons engaged in the various arts. It has meaning so far as it relates to individuals with sensitivity, imagination, creativeness, and other essentials for artistic achievement. But it is an error to assume that 'artistry' is linked with a particular type of face, hair, hand, or body. If people who are artistic do show it in any way in their looks, it is only because in the course of time they have developed certain physical traits through their ways of working, thinking, and living. In the case of any child, however, there is no way one can tell from his physical characteristics that he is or isn't a 'born' artist.

In all the arts the basic components are much the same:

the feeling for composition, form, rhythm, shadings of expression (nuances), and the more elusive aforementioned qualities of 'creativeness', 'sensitiveness', and 'imagination'. It is not improbable that these elements are much influenced by some general hereditary endowment, which may explain why artistic or creative persons usually show talents of various kinds, and often excel in several fields simultaneously. But proficiency in a specific art demands additional special abilities, and therefore special supplementary genes (as we have already seen in the case of music). The great painter must have a keen eye for colour, which would rule out the colour-blind person (although he would not be prevented, if he had great artistic ability, from being an etcher or sculptor). So, too, great fiction-writing, drama, poetry, or other arts, undoubtedly demand special sensory and personality factors, all of which may be conditioned by heredity as well as environment. Thus, a general 'artistic heredity', plus an 'artistic environment', may explain families in which many members for successive generations were outstanding in one or another of the arts. At the same time, added specific requirements may explain why some members excelled in one art form, some in another form, and some (lacking necessary key genes) showed talent in none of the arts.

The clearest indications that great talents are inborn come from studying the backgrounds and histories of true *geniuses*: the rare individuals, arising once or twice in a century, who reach the topmost levels of human achievement. Socrates, Leonardo da Vinci, Michelangelo, Shakespeare, Newton, Beethoven, Franklin, Lincoln, Edison, Einstein – these have been among them. In former times geniuses were awesomely regarded as products of supernatural and mysterious forces. Today science sees the genius as someone initially endowed with a *rare and unusual combination of superior genes*. Obviously, environment also plays a part in permitting the seeds of genius to take root and flourish. But the belief that geniuses are the products primarily of unusual heredity rests on the fact that no special type of environment can be shown to have produced them, and that geniuses have arisen in many types of environment.

Perhaps the most amazing genius of all time was Leonardo da Vinci. The illegitimate son of a Florentine peasant girl and a minor official of the fifteenth century, Leonardo as a child spontaneously displayed a bewildering variety of talents. These he proceeded to develop – many of them without training or precedent – until eventually he led his world in sculpture, painting, science, mathematics, engineering, and invention, and was also notable as a musician and a poet. There seems to be no other explanation for Leonardo except phenomenal inborn endowment. Nor can any environment explain the incredible literary and dramatic powers of Shakespeare, who, too, came from an obscure background, with little schooling and nothing exceptional in the way of opportunity.

Having already dealt with various 'talent' genes, we may now seek the answer to genius in the most potent and rarest of the human achievement genes which make possible the maximum development of human senses and mental powers. Most persons would probably not be carrying any of these genes, some persons might carry one or two; but only once in many millions of times would a couple in any generation be carrying between them all of the genes required to produce a genius. The parents themselves, each lacking some of the essential 'genius' genes, might be nobodies – which explains why geniuses so often seem to arise suddenly out of nowhere. Again, the chance that a child of a genius would receive exactly the same, or an equally remarkable combination of genes, is exceedingly remote, which could explain why successive geniuses do not follow in the same family. (Illustration, page 175.)

Are geniuses 'abnormal'? There is a long-standing belief that this is so – that geniuses must be mentally or physically abnormal in some way. In support, lists have been compiled of geniuses and near-geniuses who suffered from various mental or physical disorders: Socrates, Molière, Nietzsche, Caesar, Napoleon, Van Gogh, etc. On the other hand, it has been pointed out that many other persons of genius calibre were fully normal in every ordinary sense. As examples, of men close to our own time, and of whom we can speak with accuracy: Benjamin Franklin, Thomas Jefferson, Lincoln, Shaw, Churchill, Einstein. It remains possible that the incidence of physical and mental abnormalities may have been, and may now be, higher than average among geniuses and other highly creative persons, not because abnormality goes with their 'genius' genes, but for these reasons: (1) A person with unusual talent, who is not physically or mentally average or 'normal', may be especially likely to think in unconventional ways and do unusual things; (2) talented persons who are maladjusted, sickly, or otherwise 'different', may have an exceptional drive to 'compensate' by working feverishly towards their goals; (3) persons far in advance of their times in their thinking or creations are likely to be considered 'queer' by their contemporaries, and if this leads to added social and financial stresses, they may have an above-average chance of cracking up. Today the better understanding of the nature of genius and improved methods of educating and rearing exceptionally talented children may very well diminish such relationship as there has been between genius and 'queerness'.

Another popular belief, that geniuses tend to be short-lived, is not supported by evidence. Many geniuses in the past did die young, but this was when average life spans were short. On the other hand, many geniuses lived to very ripe old ages: Michelangelo, Titian, Rubens, Newton, Shaw, Sibelius, Matisse, Rouault. A recent analysis shows that the average longevity of thousands of geniuses and near-geniuses was no less than that of their respective generations.

While most geniuses were prodigies – children with exceptional mental powers or talents – it does not follow that every prodigy is a potential genius. Some prodigies may be 'incomplete' geniuses, endowed with only some of the required 'genius' genes (or with other mental stimuli) which may start them off in a remarkable way but not carry them too far. In other cases a prodigy is equipped with only a phenomenal memory, or quick reading and learning ability, which enables him to go through school studies by leaps and bounds. In still other cases clever and ambitious parents may succeed, by intensive training, to induce precociousness in a child. But whenever a child's reasoning ability or innate talents are also not exceptional, as is very often the case, a letdown in achievement generally results at maturity. Parents and teachers should therefore be extremely cautious about overestimating the importance of seemingly precocious mental powers or other gifts in children, and trying to force their development.

As with musical genius (to which it appears to be related in some ways), phenomenal *mathematical ability* usually appears spontaneously at very early ages, many of the greatest mathematicians – Galois and Leibnitz, and among contemporaries, Norbert Wiener and Julian Schwinger – having been prodigies. Further, while great mathematical achievement requires great intellect, mathematical aptitude of itself (again as with musical aptitude) need not be related to intelligence. Many phenomenal mental calculators had or have mediocre minds in all other respects, and some have been found among the feeble-minded, these being known as *idiot savants*. Because unusual mathematical ability has been found running in families for as many as five generations, some authorities believe it may be produced by a single dominant (or dominant-qualified) gene.

Chess-playing ability appears to be a specialized offshoot of mathematical ability, in which the traits of phenomenal memory and of visualizing complicated arrangements are principal factors. Some hereditary basis is also indicated. Thus, as with both musical and mathematical aptitude, phenomenal chess-playing aptitude appears in childhood, almost every chess master on record having been a child prodigy in the field. (The top-ranking chess player of the United States, Samuel Reshevsky, was giving chess-playing exhibitions at the age of six. The current chess phenomenon, Bobby Fischer of Brooklyn, became United States champion at fourteen.)

Coming back to *sex differences* in the arts, earlier in this chapter we touched upon the puzzling absence of women among the great composers. Equally puzzling is the fact that while women are among the fine painters and sculptors, none has achieved ranking with the very best, that is of the calibre

How Genius May Be Produced

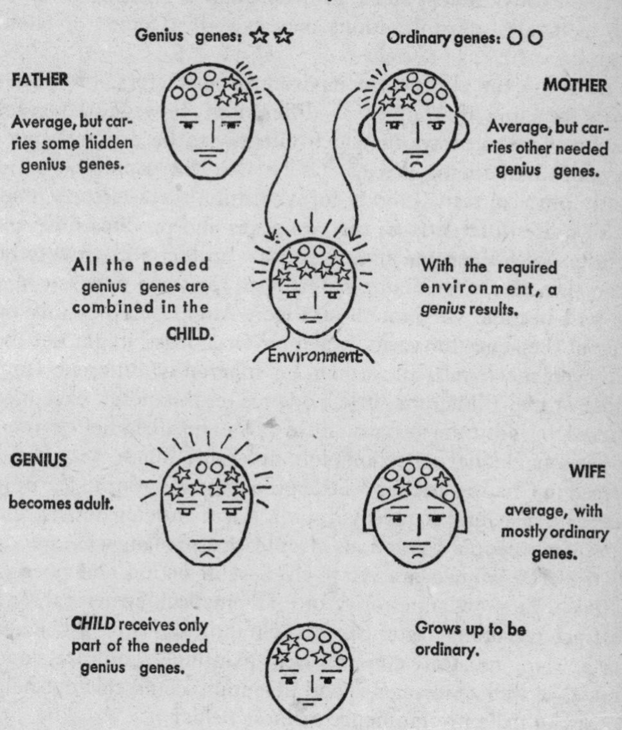

of the top old masters, or of more recent masters such as Cézanne, Picasso, Matisse, Jacob Epstein, etc. In literature, poetry, and drama, despite the many women who have made outstanding contributions, it can hardly be said that any have approached the status of Shakespeare, Molière, or Shaw. Nor in science, with full recognition of the achievements of Mme Curie, Lisa Meitner, and several others, have there as yet been any women Newtons or Einsteins. As for *inventors*, one finds virtually no women among them. How explain this? It has been argued that the reasons are entirely environmental: that women in the past never had equal opportunity to develop in the creative fields, and that even today a great many more disadvantages and inhibitions may exist for women of talent than for men.

Allowing for all adverse environmental factors, the possibility remains that inherent differences between the sexes might affect the ways in which talents can be expressed and developed in them. We have seen that the same genes for many physical traits – body form, stature, disease, etc. – may work quite differently in the two sexes and produce different results. With the same stature genes a brother will grow to be several inches taller than a sister; with the same muscle genes he will become very much stronger. Might this possibly be true of the genes for various talents? Or at least, might not the achievement *trends* of women be inherently different from those of men? There is little evidence on this point, except as offered by aptitude tests of little boys and girls before their environments have become too different. These tests (discussed in Chapter 19) show little girls to be superior in learning to speak, read, and acquire vocabularies, in noticing details, and in sensing people's reactions. Could this explain why among all the arts, women are relatively best in fiction and poetry? Little boys show superiority in mathematical, structural, and abstract reasoning tests. Since such aptitudes are highly important in musical composition, painting, sculpture, and drama, as well as in science and invention, could this not help to explain male pre-eminence in these fields?

Whatever the present arguments or limited facts, it is not likely that with women constituted differently from men by inborn factors, and with the probability that they will also continue to be reared, trained, and employed differently in many ways, we will ever have complete answers as to what their relative abilities may be. A guess that might be made is that women's drives and capacities are not the same as men's, and that they therefore have been at a disadvantage in following male formulas and methods, and trying to compete with men in precisely the same types of achievement. Perhaps as women express *themselves* more, and have increased opportunities to develop such special gifts as they may have, their creative achievements will become ever greater. For the present it is already evident that growing numbers of women are forging ahead in all creative fields, with many of them excelling a large proportion of the men in the same fields.

CHAPTER TWENTY-ONE

BEHAVIOUR

THE MOST IMPORTANT thing about human individuals in relation to one another is how they *behave*. Is a person pleasant or unpleasant? Calm or hot-tempered? Kind or cruel? Decent or viciously criminal? Lazy or enterprising? Timid or aggressive? And so on. We have seen that heredity governs people's looks, and to a great extent their body-functioning and intelligence. Does heredity also destine or incline individuals to behave in specific ways? An immediate difficulty in answering is that we know human behaviour differs greatly in different environments, and that even the behaviour of the same person varies considerably at different stages of life and under different conditions. Nevertheless, as we shall see, beneath the layer of outside influences there quite probably are differences in people's behaviour 'machinery' that may strongly affect their acts, personalities, and reactions to others.

If there are any inherited behaviour tendencies in human beings, these must be similar to what we call 'instincts' in lower animals. 'Instinct' refers to an *inborn* tendency to do things or behave in certain ways without training. Some psychologists dislike using the term on the ground that the behaviour of lower animals even in a natural state may be considerably influenced by experience, learning from their elders, and changes in environment. In place of 'instincts', terms such as 'conditioned reflexes', 'stimuli', 'drives', etc., are suggested. But this may be quibbling. For most authorities, and for the general reader, it is clear that each species throughout its long history had and has its own spontaneous (unlearned) ways of courting and mating, building nests or shelters, seeking and selecting food, caring for young, getting along with its own kind, reacting to enemies, etc. Whether we think of bees, beavers, bears, bunnies, bulls, bullfinches, bluefish, boas, baboons, billy goats, or butterflies, we can identify with members of each species particular types of *inborn* behaviour which are almost as much a part of them as are the shapes of their heads and bodies.

People, too, constantly speak of their 'instincts': 'He has the "right" instinct'; 'Her instinct told her'; 'They instinctively liked each other,' etc. And, in a general way, we refer to 'human' or 'inhuman instincts'. In the earliest stages of mankind the behaviour of humans undoubtedly was governed by as many, if not more, instincts as those in lower animals. We can be sure that humans, as well, started off with inborn behaviour patterns which directed their mating, caring for their young, selecting and securing food, fighting or avoiding enemies, etc. Otherwise they could not have gone far on the road to survival. Any genes governing such instincts which human beings had we probably still have in great measure today. But the biggest difference between human beings and lower animals is that, going with our superior brains, we also have the capacity to control, modify, and train our instincts, and at the same time to change and improve our environments so that the need for our instincts would be lessened. Thus, as civilization has progressed and as life and training have become increasingly complex, the human instincts have been pushed farther into the background as only *starting points* for behaviour.

Aiding the environmental influences on human behaviour is the fact that the period of dependency – before offspring become mature and can lead their own lives – is greater for humans than for other animals, giving parents much more opportunity to train their children. Among apes, however, the period of childhood is almost as great (chimpanzees and gorillas not reaching puberty until the age of about nine or ten). So for the most part, it is still the inherited flexibility of the human mind and its capacity for being moulded that permits training and experience to influence our behaviour.

Evidence that the 'instinct' genes have not been bred out of us can be seen when we watch infants. As babies come into the world, inborn tendencies to behave in definite ways show themselves in how they feed, move, grab, smile, etc. Moreover, there seems to be an inherited 'time-clock' mechanism that sets off given types of behaviour at given stages: when the baby will first begin to bubble, coo; turn over, sit up; observe and grab things; walk; respond to language, talk, be ready for toilet training, etc. This behaviour is common to babies among all peoples, civilized and primitive. It is taken so much for granted that when babies anywhere fail to react in the expected ways at the appropriate stages, parents rightfully worry. At the same time, it is also expected and noted that (within the prescribed limits) particular babies will behave in particular ways. In fact, any two babies of the same mother are apt to be no more alike in what they do and when they do it than in their looks. But we know that the individual behaviour patterns of infants are much more conditioned than are their looks by their experiences in the womb, and by many subtle influences after they are born. So we can be far less sure of the part that heredity may play in producing these individual differences than of its effects either on infants' looks or on their general patterns of behaviour.

As in infancy, so in later ages and among peoples of all kinds, we can see certain similar patterns of behaviour: mothers nursing and fondling their young; little males wrestling or fighting older males; youths or adult males strutting or performing to impress females, and females acting coyly, flirtatiously, or enticingly; two males violently aroused and battling over a female; groups of individuals trustingly following a dominant leader, etc. All such behaviour is paralleled in lower animals. More important, various scientific studies and experiments have linked this, and other kinds of behaviour in lower animals, with biological factors often found to be hereditary. Animals have been bred in which one or another of these 'social' traits is expressed in greater or lesser degree. Also, marked changes in such types of behaviour can be produced in individual animals by causing an increase or decrease in the production of certain hormones, or by operating on certain brain and nerve centres. How far this applies to human beings is uncertain, but here are some interesting findings:

Parental behaviour, we know, appears in many different forms, and degrees of parental instincts appear among lower animals. In humans we also speak of 'natural-born' mothers or fathers; or 'motherly' or 'fatherly' types, and their opposites. But while in lower animals it is clear that parental behaviour is largely governed by hormonal stimuli and other biological factors, among human beings individual differences in this respect appear to be conditioned mainly by social and psychological influences. However, some authorities report that degrees of 'motherliness' among women tend to go with certain physical factors which show themselves in breast types, hip forms, menstrual functioning, etc., as well as with certain types of behaviour recognizable even in young girls.

Are some human beings born to be bossed and others to be leaders (irrespective of intelligence)? Among various animal species it has been found that individuals in any group can be graded according to degrees of dominance or submissiveness. In most flocks of birds or poultry a 'peck order' can be observed: a given bird pecks at another which submits, but which in turn can peck submissive birds lower in the scale. In groups of apes, mice, and perhaps even dogs (according to a recent study) similar rankings of dominance and submissiveness may be found. Also proved or indicated is that when the hormonal make-up of the individual is changed by treatment or operation, his or her standing in the 'dominance order' also changes. It may be guessed that in human beings, too, hormonal states – inborn or otherwise – influence the dominance feelings and behaviour of individuals towards others. But how far the biology, rather than psychology, of persons is involved in most of their relationships remains to be established.

As with dominance, degrees of aggressiveness or lack of it have been found conditioned in lower animals by their hormonal workings and brain functioning, differences in which can be hereditary. In human individuals, also, varying internal states contribute to their feeling 'high' or 'low', pugnacious or docile, on occasions. But again, since psychological factors can produce the same results, it may be very difficult in any given case to show that these traits in persons have a hereditary basis.

Tendencies to special types of *fears* are inherited by each lower animal species, and help to protect them against their natural enemies or hazards. One can only assume that buried deep in the human unconscious there also are inherited fear tendencies that aided our remote ancestors. But in modern individuals most fears have been shown by psychologists to be conditioned by personal experiences, often in the earliest years. Even women's fears of mice or snakes, which were once considered instinctive, appear to be mostly psychological and easily overcome by training, as is proved in many college laboratories where girl students work unconcernedly with these animals.

The responses of persons to tastes, smells, sounds, pain, and colour affect their everyday behaviour and social relationships in many ways, and for this reason are extensively studied by psychologists. That heredity plays an important part in sensory reactions is obvious, most clearly so in the case of the lower animals, each species of which is characterized by its own special sensory equipment. Among human beings, inheritance of individual sensory differences of various kinds are undoubtedly also much influenced by heredity, but specific facts on this point are still scanty.

One trait that has been given much study is 'taste blindness' with respect to the chemical PTC (*phenylthiocarbamide*), which has been found inherited through simple recessive genes. About seven out of ten persons who taste paper impregnated with this chemical say it is 'bitter', whereas the rest (those who carry two recessive 'non-tasting' genes) detect almost no taste. Possible hereditary differences have also been reported in tasting other chemical substances, which may be related to various foods.

Smelling defects, involving the inability to smell some substances, if not most substances, are usually due to nasal diseases, infections, or injuries. However, where total inability to smell runs in families, it may be the rare inherited condition of *anosmia*, caused by a dominant gene.

Differences in response to *pain*, with some individuals almost insensitive to it, have on occasions been reported as influenced by heredity.

Hereditary abnormalities or deficiencies in the visual senses (notably in colour vision) and in the auditory senses (including 'musical ear'), have previously been discussed. Otherwise, while a considerable range of difference is apparent among individuals in sensitivity to foods, perfumes and odours, pain, noise, drugs, etc., the role of heredity with respect to these differences remains to be clarified. Such investigation is not easy, because of the fact that the development of the human senses in given directions – as in the preferences for or aversions to given foods, odours, or colours – and the degrees to which tastes express themselves, are much influenced by training and individual psychological factors.

CHAPTER TWENTY-TWO

PERSONALITY AND TEMPERAMENT

BY PERSONALITY we mean the sum of a human individual's behaviour traits, *plus* all the other special qualities of mind, body, sex, and social adjustment that distinguish him as a particular *person.* Second, personality refers to qualities developed by one person in relation to other persons. Strictly speaking, then, only human beings can be considered as having personalities. Although we might like to think that cats, dogs, and other animals also have personalities, scientists prefer to speak of their traits as behaviour patterns. A distinction is that behaviour traits are simpler, and as we have seen, can be almost directly inherited in lower animals in the form of instincts. It is far less certain whether any personality traits are ever directly inherited.

Human infants, like other little animals, come into the world with inherited behaviour patterns, as noted in the last chapter. But from the moment they begin to be trained and influenced by their parents, older children, nurses, and other human beings, they cease to be merely instinctive creatures, and any inborn tendencies become only the raw materials from which the forces outside of them mould their personalities. How far the inherited tendencies can push their way through the conditioning forces, and stay on top, is a question. Some studies (Dr M. M. Shirley, Dr Patricia Neilon) which have followed the same individuals from infancy through adolescence, indicate that in most cases those who were especially good-natured, alert, aggressive, difficult, etc. (or the opposite), tended to have the same personality traits in later years. Many mothers will confirm this in their children. But theories that children's personalities are greatly affected by whether they were breast fed or bottle fed, weaned early or late, toilet-trained one way or another, continue to be debated, without conclusive findings.

In addition to the obvious mental and nervous disorders, a great many inherited diseases, defects, and organic weaknesses or peculiarities have characteristic effects on personality. Persons suffering from migraine headaches, for example, have been reported as tending to show 'intolerance, perfectionism, sexual difficulties, etc.' Particular personality patterns may also go with glandular disorders, allergies, vitamin deficiencies, digestive disturbances, and other conditions in which heredity may play a part. Changes in the body's chemical state or functioning by means of various drugs, and operations on the brain and nervous system, have been shown to affect personality in many ways. One may assume, then, that any inherited differences – large or small – in the workings of the glands and other organs would account for some degree of difference in the personalities of individuals. The body's chemical transitions at adolescence, during the menopause in women, and in ageing, also have their definite effects on personality. But very probably, beneath the outer personality layers of individuals which can be much affected by changes in health or other factors, there is always an *inner core* of personality which persists through life. And it is this 'inner personality' which may be strongly directed by inherited tendencies.

People have always believed that certain looks go with certain personalities. From Shakespeare's plays through to modern novels, dramas, movies, comic strips, and TV shows, one will find people with given types of faces and bodies cast as characters with given personality traits: heroines, fair, slim, and lovely; heroes, tall, straight, and handsome; villains, lean and swarthy; redheads, fiery natures; bold men with jutting jaws, weaklings with receding chins; sneaky people with warped bodies, etc. Science has found no such connexion between genes for looks and genes for personality, character, or temperament. The only exceptions are in certain inherited diseases and abnormal conditions (discussed in earlier chapters)

Looks and Personality

All of these notions are wrong!

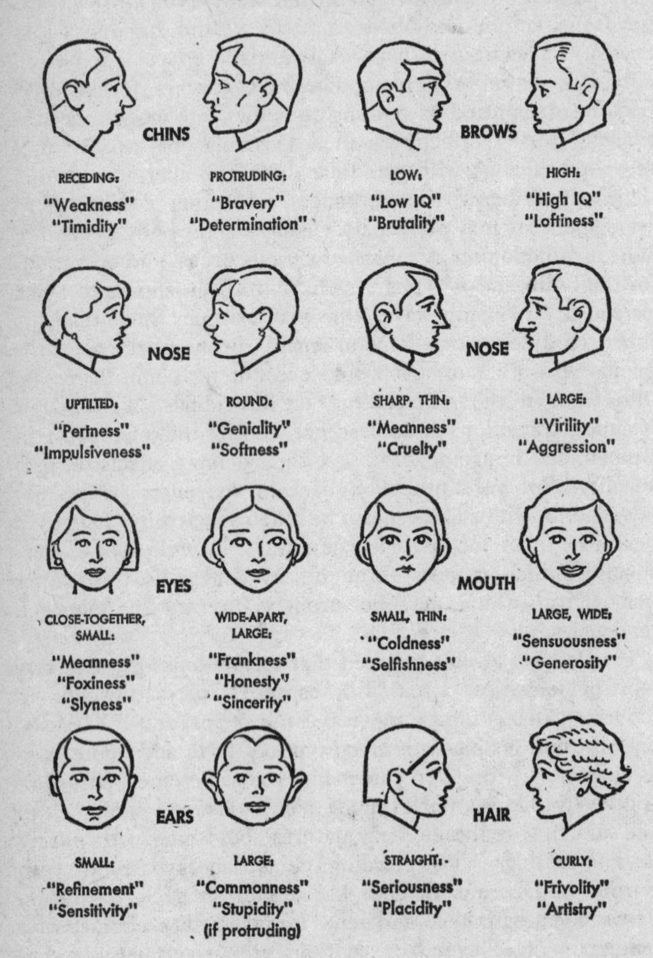

The genes that determine physical traits need not at all be related to the genes that affect personality traits. (See text.)

which may together affect both outward appearance and behaviour. Otherwise almost any kind of nose, eyes, mouth, complexion, colouring, or other bodily detail can go with any kind of inborn personality tendency. However, *facial expressions* involve something else. The way a person has used and uses his mouth and eyes may offer real clues to his personality, as many also movements of the head, body, hands, etc.

In recent years the theory has been revived that given types of body build, *somatotypes*, do in a general way go with given types of personality and temperament, presumably because the same glandular and other factors which affect body build also may produce certain behaviour tendencies. (This would in turn bring heredity into the picture so far as it governs these glandular and other workings.) One of the first to claim this relationship was Dr E. Kretschmer, who classified people as 'pyknic' (fat), 'aesthenic' (lean), and 'athletic' types, ascribing certain general personality characteristics to each. More recently Dr W. H. Sheldon has devised these classifications: *endomorphs* (soft, round physiques, tending to obesity) – 'inclined to be home-loving, placid, sociable'; *mesomorphs* (athletic, muscular, heavy-boned) – 'likely to be fighters, leaders, heroes, lovers of thrills and action'; *ectomorphs* (slim, flat-chested, stringy-muscled) – 'inclined to be "mental" and alert, but not too aggressive, forward, or at ease with people.' Various gradations and in-between types of physiques are rated by how much of each 'morph' component there is in an individual's body build. Many psychiatrists consider these classifications helpful in diagnoses (if used with other evidence). But authorities differ as to their dependability, and especially, as to whether they can be related to *inherited* personality traits.

Still persisting and taken seriously are old notions, that different 'areas' or parts of the face and head are in some way tied up with specific mental traits, and therefore can reveal character. For instance, that 'development of various areas of the nose reflect capacity for observation, imagination, etc.'; or that in the areas of the temple and eyebrows one can read such and such other traits. To this, as to 'phrenology', which purports to read character through bumps on the head, reputable scientists say, simply: 'Bunk'.

While heredity may couple any kind of feature or looks with any kind of personality trait, people themselves tend to ignore this fact. As a result, personalities can be much affected by how looks are regarded. If a little girl is drooled over because she's 'so pretty', she certainly won't develop the same personality as will a homely sister. Similarly, to the extent that people react differently to tall or short persons, slender or fat ones, blondes and brunettes, the fair-skinned or dark-skinned, or to this or that kind of mouth or nose, the individuals' personalities will also develop differently.

But it is important to remember that attitudes towards the very same types of looks – nose size, hip size, leg shape, skin colour – may differ greatly in different groups, and when they do, so do the effects on personalities. Fat women in the United States are made to feel inferior, slim women to feel superior; but in some parts of the Orient and Africa the plumpest women are the glamour girls, and the slim ones are the wall-flowers. A few decades ago girls with small bosoms were most approved among Americans (as they still are among Japanese), and those with large bosoms self-consciously tried to strap them down. As need hardly be said, there's been a change. So, too, the small, cupid's-bow mouth has currently yielded in desirability to the full, large mouth; and increases in stature have revised the scale by which persons are rated and feel themselves 'too tall' or 'too short'. The genes for looks remain the same generation after generation, but their effects on personalities may be almost anything that people wish to make them.

Another exploded notion is that thick, large hands and ankles betoken peasant or common ancestry, and a coarse personality, whereas slim hands and ankles go with 'aristocratic' or genteel ancestry and inherent refinement. It is true that people who do heavy manual work in time develop thicker hands and ankles than those who do not, but these effects cannot be passed on through inheritance; and if the descendants themselves no longer do heavy work, they may have just as slim hands or ankles as those of 'aristocratic' blood. Apart from the direct effects of work and living habits, the sizes, shapes, or textures of hands and feet have no relationship to personality factors.

Moreover, despite claims of palmists and their writings (and the enormous number of people who believe them), science has found absolutely no relationship between specific lines in palms and any inborn traits of personality, mental qualities, success tendencies, or what not. Even more, the belief that anyone can predict future events (whom one will marry, how long one will live, or how many children one may have) by 'reading' palm lines is pure superstition. Clever palmists may sometimes make good guesses, but only as any keen observer might do, not by looking at the palms but by noting details of a person's general appearance, behaviour, and speech.

Characteristic movements of the mouth, eyes, hands, and head, or ways of walking, praying, etc., observed in groups of people from the same stocks, countries, or localities, almost invariably result from formed habits, and are no more hereditary than are their languages or accents. Likewise, those in given occupations (farmers, policemen, sailors, actresses, etc.) develop distinctive ways of gesturing and moving. Children, in turn, tend consciously or unconsciously to imitate their parents, so it is not surprising to find certain mannerisms running in families. However, there are cases where some odd or unusual gesture or movement of a parent seems to appear spontaneously in a child (as in a son who has never seen his father). This leaves open the possibility that such mannerisms may arise through inherited muscular reflexes. Adding to the theory are findings at Jackson Memorial Laboratory that different breeds of dogs have their characteristic involuntary movements.

Astrology is mentioned here only because so many millions of people who read astrology books and consult astrologers or astrological horoscopes sincerely believe that their personalities were and are dictated, and their fortunes governed by, the stars they were 'born under'. It may shock or anger them to be told that true scientists regard astrology as no science at all, but, like palmistry, as mere superstition. Incidentally, one should not confuse astrology with astronomy (although in ancient times the two were linked). Astronomy is now the recognized science that deals with the stars and planets, and their movements. But astronomers reject all the hocus-pocus going with astrology, and some years ago one of their official committees (headed by Harvard professor Bart J. Bok) flatly stated that 'astrology is a magical practice which has no shred of justification in fact'. Note, for example, that among twins the fact that they were 'born under the same star' by no means makes their personalities or fortunes the same – particularly if they are fraternal twins who may be as different in personality as any two children of a family born under different stars.

Going further with studies of twins, some light on the inheritance of personality has come through analyses of separate traits as shown by identical twins (who have the same hereditary factors), as compared with fraternal twins (who differ in hereditary make-up). On the other hand, even among identicals reared together, it is frequently noted that there can be considerable difference in personality between members of a pair as a result of environmentally produced differences in physical make-up, health, or experiences. In major respects many personality traits of identical twins are usually much alike, whereas those of fraternal twins are not. It is true that identical twins are reared more closely together. However, remarkable similarities in traits have also developed in identical twins separated in early infancy and reared widely apart in different localities and types of homes.

Two studies reported in 1955 tend to strengthen the personality-inheritance theory. One by Drs Raymond B. Cattell, Duncan B. Blewett, and John R. Beloff, involved comparisons of personality traits of almost a thousand individuals, among them scores of identical and fraternal twin pairs, and of non-twin members of many families. The findings led to these conclusions: heredity may play a leading role in making some persons more easygoing, sociable, and warmhearted, or bolder and more outgoing, than others. But environment predominates in producing a happy-go-lucky nature and impulsiveness. In another study, Dr Steven G. Vandenberg compared personality traits of forty-five pairs of identical and thirty-seven of fraternal twins (all high-school students). He found so much more similarity between the identicals in response to music and art, and in degrees of self-confidence and stubbornness, as to conclude that heredity must be strongly involved in producing these traits.

Personality studies of the Dionne quintuplets were made only in their early years. Certain differences in their personalities were observed, but these were for the most part no greater than those which parents recognize between any two identical twins. However, limited recent information has indicated that some of the initial differences persisted and became strongly marked in the later ages, particularly with respect to Marie, and to the late Emilie (who died in 1954). As noted in Chapter 5, these two were almost like a pair of twins within the set of five, probably having been the last to develop from the same final subdivision of the egg. Marie was the weakest, sickliest, and shyest, while Emilie was epileptic, and both were less poised and less well adjusted than the other three. The two, also, had entered convents, then given up the plan to become nuns. At this writing (1961) Marie is married, as are Annette and Cecile, but Yvonne is still to be married.

The divergence among the Dionnes – despite their all having exactly the same hereditary factors – is only a partial indication of how far any inherited personality tendencies may be influenced by environment. At the same time, their personality differences have been and are probably much less than their similarities, as compared with any equal group of girls taken at random, or even any four or five separately born sisters reared in the same way. Altogether, the facts about the Dionnes, and other findings discussed in this and preceding chapters, warrant only these conclusions: there undoubtedly are genes which incline individuals to develop personalities in given directions, and different from those of other individuals, when environmental factors are the same. Any such 'personality' genes, however, are far less direct, definite, or forceful in their workings, and much more likely to be swerved off course, than are the genes for the physical traits or mental capacities. In sum, heredity provides only the raw materials for personality development. But these same raw materials in any person can be processed, shaped, and packaged in a great many different ways.

CHAPTER TWENTY-THREE

CRIMINAL BEHAVIOUR

IT IS AN old belief that 'evil streaks' or 'criminal taints' run in certain families, and also, that some human groups, nationalities, or races are more 'criminal' by nature than others. No scientific evidence for this has yet been produced. Further, there are only guesses or suppositions about the extent to which individuals in any group may inherit tendencies towards criminality. On the other hand, we can now refute or question many of the earlier theories about criminal inheritance. It is these *disproofs* regarding criminality that are perhaps most important.

What is the 'criminal type'? Our first difficulty in trying to find out whether criminality is inborn is to decide what we mean by it. Legal and social definitions of criminality vary and have varied enormously, depending on places or periods. Nor can we distinguish between criminals and non-criminals merely on the basis of those who have or haven't been convicted of wrongdoing, since law and justice are far from always the same. But even when a person's acts are so consistently vicious and antisocial as to clearly stamp him a criminal, we still have to dig deeply into his background, make-up, and thinking before we can assume that his heredity may be in any way responsible. Finally, the many types of crime – murder, robbery, rape, drug addiction, tax evasion, fraud, etc. – may often be completely unrelated; and even the same crimes (as murders, or sex offences) may be of many different types in nature and motive. To find genes causing criminality in general might be as impossible as to find genes for disease in general. Only when we examine separately each form of crime and those committing it can we begin to see what causative forces might be at work.

Keeping in mind the foregoing reservations, there is nevertheless some basis for believing that certain persons might be especially predisposed to commit crimes of various kinds, or of specific kinds, because of inborn quirks. The evidence to support this, however, is only circumstantial or inferential. For example, studies of crime among twins have shown that where they were identicals (with the same hereditary factors), if one was criminal, so was the other in at least four out of five cases, whereas in fraternal twins (with different heredity) this was true in only about one in three. But when weighing this evidence one must remember that identical twins are usually reared more closely together, and one influences the other more than is true of fraternal twins.

Where acts of violence or other crimes arise through mental diseases, such as schizophrenia, manic-depressive insanity, or psychopathic personality, heredity obviously is involved to the extent that it plays a part in these diseases. There is also limited recent evidence that a disproportionate number of criminals have abnormal brain-wave patterns, the findings being clearest in the cases of those who have committed murders, violence, or acts of cruelty on sudden impulses and without rational motivation. However, the majority of criminals show no symptoms of diseased minds, and appear to be no more than warped products of unfortunate conditioning, experiences, and circumstances.

Authorities are also finding less and less connexion between low intelligence and crime. A generation ago about 35 per cent of the prison inmates were feeble-minded and (as with insanity) where heredity could be blamed for the mental defect it might also be blamed for the criminal acts. Today, with better care and training, and more good institutional homes, fewer of the mentally retarded get into trouble or reach prisons. As a result, Dr David Wechsler, IQ expert, tells us that the IQ's of present-day prison inmates are close to the general average, with many (particularly forgers and 'white-collar' offenders) being of high intelligence. In some places average IQ's of prison inmates may continue to be low if the least intelligent are the ones most likely to be arrested and convicted, as was commonly true in the past.

Recent studies point to deviations from the average in the body chemistry of criminals as a group, leading some authorities to believe that chemical factors may be an unbalancing influence and a motivating force towards certain types of antisocial or criminal acts. Among such factors cited are sugar deficiency in the blood (*hypoglycaemia*), which may impair sensory reactions and judgements, and increase aggressiveness; calcium deficiency, making persons extremely sensitive and quick to violence; and various glandular disorders which affect the brain and behaviour of persons.

Findings have been reported from time to time that criminals as a group differ from non-criminals in features of body build. But as was stated in the preceding chapter, there is no evidence that any inherited facial or bodily detail goes with any particular behaviour trait (other than in rare cases where defective genes produce both physical and mental abnormalities). Thus, most authorities have viewed sceptically successive theories (Lombroso, Hooton, etc.) that persons committing crimes of given kinds tend to have such and such ears, eyes, foreheads, mouths, chins, or noses. Where there is any recognizable 'criminal' look, it is perhaps only because of the person's expressions and the set of the face, resulting from habits. Most recently there have been the 'body-build' theories – that criminals, or juvenile delinquents, tend to have characteristic somatotypes (types of bodies). This has also been questioned, although it is possible that since some types of crime tend to be committed more often in some groups than other groups, any differences among these groups in body build would be reflected in the criminal population.

Whatever part heredity may play in crime is greatly overshadowed by the effects of environment. This is clearly proved by the enormous differences in the rates of crime among people of the same stock, from one generation to the next, or in one locality as compared with another, as their conditions, training, and attitudes change. A striking example is the *murder* rate. Among Americans, murders were for decades far more common than among their European relatives with the same heredity. This included the Germans, who were long regarded as the most civilized, law-abiding, and disciplined of peoples. But during the mad period of Nazi rule, the murders and vicious crimes of every kind in Germany reached staggering totals. Nor is there doubt that if Americans or other people were engulfed by the same kind of psychological madness, crime would be equally rampant among them. Again, looking within the United States itself, we find tremendous differences in the murder and crime rates of different regions, states, and cities, and in neighbourhoods of the same city, even though the people may all be of similar hereditary make-up. As a general rule, regardless of people's heredity, crime rates are highest wherever social and psychological conditions are worst, the government and police most corrupt and inefficient, and the public most tolerant towards wrongdoing.

Drastic increases in crimes and lawlessness among young people in the United States and other countries during and since World War II are further proof of environmental influences. Formerly the chief causes of delinquency were considered to be poverty, bad social conditions, broken homes, etc. More recently, since delinquency has also mounted among children from the most privileged and educated groups, attention is turning as well to psychological and emotional factors, inside and outside the homes. However, the fact that under any given condition only some young people become delinquent and most others do not, and some commit horrible crimes difficult to explain, raises the possibility of inborn tendencies or predispositions in many instances. Moreover, as noted in a preceding section, *What is the 'criminal type'?* one must distinguish between different types of delinquency. Those involving sex offences, or theft, or drug addiction, or assaults, or vicious behaviour, may be quite unrelated, and in some the possibility of hereditary tendencies may be greater than in others. There is much in this area that scientists need to explore before definite answers can be given.

While rates for crime as a whole, and for specific crimes, vary greatly among persons of different foreign stocks and races in the United States, this, too, may well be traced to the different conditions under which they have been reared, their traditions, occupations, and habits. There are times when persons may feel ashamed or disturbed because given types of crime seem unduly prevalent among individuals of their own race, religion, or ethnic group. But this may have no more to do with their genes than corned beef and cabbage has to do with Irish genes, sauerbraten with German genes, kosher salami with Jewish genes, spaghetti with Italian genes, etc. Thus, crime differences among Americans of all origins have tended to diminish or disappear as their ways of living and habits have become the same.

The higher *recorded* crime rate of American Negroes as compared with whites also has nothing to do with inherent differences, in the opinion of qualified authorities. Reasons given include the inferior conditions under which Negroes have lived and still live, on the average; discriminations against them, and less chance to get adequate legal help, which make them more likely than whites to run afoul of laws, be arrested, convicted, sentenced; and various other environmental factors which work adversely against Negro family life, proper child rearing, and individual adjustment. Wherever economic, educational, and social conditions for Negroes improve, their crime rates drop.

Currently there is also concern in some American cities (New York and others) about the high crime and delinquency rates among recently arrived large groups of Puerto Ricans. Any thought that this is related to 'natural' tendencies, or to anything other than their extremely underprivileged living conditions, is questionable. Few authorities doubt that, as with the Negroes, the crime rates among these new arrivals will drop steadily as their environments and opportunities improve.

In all human groups, the marked *sex differences* in crime are of particular interest. Both heredity and environment are peculiarly interrelated in producing the vastly higher rate of crime among males than among females, and the differences in types of crime, as measured by arrests and convictions. Recent figures in the United States show eight times as many men as women arrested. For *murder*, the male rate is six times that of the female; for *burglary*, fifty times; *robbery*, twenty-two times; *forgery*, five times. Even then, this excess of male over female crime is much smaller than it was in former times, when women had less freedom to adopt men's bad habits and practices. But the question remains, whether training, moral codes, and other conditioning factors can completely account for the sex differences in crime.

The theory that men by nature are more inclined to commit crimes of violence than are women, everything else being equal, rests on these facts: (1) Among other animals – all mammals and most birds – males are inherently more aggressive, more given to violent behaviour, and harder to train or domesticate; (2) experiments with lower animals have shown a direct relationship between male hormones and aggressiveness: treating females (rats, hens, etc.) with male hormones makes them develop male aggressive and fighting qualities, while in males, subtracting male hormones through castration, or adding female hormones, tends to make them more passive and submissive; (3) in the youngest children one can note a greater tendency of boys to be aggressive, unruly, and destructive; (4) superior strength and physical capacities of men lead them more into occupations inducing violence and familiarity with weapons; (5) differences in sexual functioning, in their natural parental roles and in the consequences of loose conduct, tend to make women more restrained than males in their behaviour, and further differentiate their activities, opportunities, and inclinations with respect to crime.

The foregoing points, as noted, apply mainly to crimes involving physical acts. There is no evidence that nature or heredity have made women any more moral or angelic than men. The crimes of women almost always have tended to be more subtle, veiled, and personal, and more likely to evade the meshes of the law, than those of men. But as their opportunities for open wrongdoing have increased, women's crime rates have shot upwards. Thus, the introduction of firearms, eliminating the strength disadvantages, has caused a marked rise in murders by women; and occupational changes have greatly increased the convictions of women for theft, fraud, forgery, embezzlement, etc.

Differences in the sex organs and sex functioning of males and females lead naturally to differences in the types of sex crimes each might commit (mainly, *rape* by males and *prostitution* by females). Otherwise, however, there is little relationship between heredity and sex offences. Nor, as a rule, are sex offences linked with other types of crime, except in so far as criminal conduct or a criminal environment may also lead to looseness or viciousness in sexual conduct. This is especially true of prostitution. In countries where prostitutes are not regarded as criminal (or in some places not even looked down on), there may be nothing in the way of abnormal tendencies to turn them towards this profession. But wherever prostitution is condemned by law and society, and where it is conducted in a criminal atmosphere, women who go into it, and stay in it, do tend to have abnormal criminal tendencies. However, prostitution by itself, and other sex offences (including *homosexuality*), might be more properly considered as types of sexual behaviour. (See next chapter.)

Alcoholism is mentioned here only because it continues to be classified as a crime in many legal statutes. However, most authorities now regard this not as a crime or any ordinary form of wrongdoing, but as a disease or personality disorder. At the same time, new theories have increased the possibility that heredity may be involved in *some* cases of alcoholism. That the condition is largely environmental is clearly shown by the enormous differences in the rate of alcoholism in various countries, nationalities, regions, and social groups, as governed by their habits, attitudes, and religious precepts; and by the great increase in alcoholism among women and young people since social codes became looser. But to explain why in any group only *certain* individuals become alcoholics under the same conditions which leave others unaffected, recent studies indicate these possibilities: that the chemical make-up of some individuals is such as to either induce an unusual craving for alcohol, perhaps because of certain dietary and vitamin deficiencies, or to cause them to react abnormally to its effects; and/or that easily unbalanced mental and emotional states in some individuals predispose them to become alcoholics under little more than ordinary stresses. In either of these situations there could be hereditary factors producing or increasing the tendencies. For the present this is only theory. Until proved otherwise, one may assume that wherever alcoholism runs in a family (grandfather, father, son, mother, daughter, etc.), it is most likely that the members have *acquired* the habit from one another.

Most of the facts with respect to crime in individuals can be applied to refuting the theory that in mankind as a whole there are 'mass criminal' or 'murder' instincts, which must burst out periodically into war; and that these 'instincts' for war or aggression are very strong in some nations, whereas peoples of other nations are by nature peaceful. This theory finds no support either in scientific studies or recent history. A first error is to assume that war is a 'return to the animal state'. Actually, while among lower animals *individuals* may fight, there is never any bloody mass conflict between two groups of the same species, as there is among human beings. Again, if in lower animals, those of different species or breeds are most antagonistic, so among humans one would expect any 'war instinct' to show itself most between those of different races. Yet we know that many of the bloodiest wars in history have been between groups of the same race, and often also of the same stocks and nationalities (as in the civil wars in the United States and most recently, in Korea, Indo-China, and China).

Finally, the presumed warlike or peaceful nature of any people has often changed abruptly. Many primitive tribes (including American Indians) once considered bloodthirsty savages are now among the most peaceful of peoples. So, too, are the once-warlike Scandinavians. The Chinese, for centuries peaceful, are now highly war-minded. The Jews, warriors in Biblical times, were long thereafter thought of as non-fighters, but back in Israel have again become warriors. And so on. All of this has led the scientists who study human make-up to be among those most convinced that warfare lies not in our genes but in our thinking, and that if there is any 'mass' instinct among human groups, it is for getting along with rather than killing one another. This might even be applied to crimes by individuals: the strongest desire in everyone is to get along with others – to be loved and respected, to be given a chance to be useful, to 'belong' and to join both in producing and receiving whatever the community can provide for happiness. It is only when individuals are in some way frustrated in achieving this end that they turn to crime.

CHAPTER TWENTY-FOUR

SEX AND SEXUAL BEHAVIOUR

THE MOST IMPORTANT of all influences on behaviour is a person's sex. Just as among lower animals the male and female of each species differ in their behaviour in many ways, so do they also among human beings. These human behaviour differences may be classed under two headings: (1) *Sex* behaviour, referring to distinguishing traits of males as compared with females in actions, mannerisms, speech, movements, attitudes, etc.; (2) *Sexual* behaviour, directly involving the sexual impulses, feelings, and acts, as they reveal themselves in love-making, intercourse, and other sexual outlets. Both types of behaviour are the extremely complex results of an interplay between inborn tendencies and environmental influences. Our purpose in this chapter will be mainly to look for possible hereditary factors.

At the moment of conception, as reported in Chapter 4, the XY sex chromosome combination of males, and the XX combination of females, start them off immediately on different developmental roads. Further, as reported in other chapters, with succeeding stages of development the sexes show marked differences in their growth rates, body form and functioning, onset of puberty, physical capacities, sexual organs, reproductive and parental roles, susceptibility to diseases and defects, ageing effects and other biological manifestations. Not the least of these are the processes peculiar to women: menstruation, childbearing, child-nursing, and the menopause. Even if every effort were made to equalize the external environments for both sexes, each of the factors mentioned would tend to produce some differences in the behaviour of females generally as compared with males. However, we must not ignore the fact that environment may continually work to intensify and sometimes distort these differences through training, moral and religious codes, courtship patterns, marriages roles, jobs, styles, etc.

Among the biological factors most directly affecting male and female behaviour are the differences in the sex hormones – not in type, but in quantity. Males produce much more of the so-called male hormone – *androgen*; females produce much more of the so-called female hormone – *oestrogen.* (Some of the other hormones – pituitary, adrenal, thyroid – also may be produced by the two sexes in different proportions.) In lower animals the sex-hormone effects on behaviour are striking. In poultry, when young female chicks are dosed with male hormones, they begin to act like little roosters, showing sudden aggressiveness and trying to crow; grown hens, if deprived of female hormones, also take on rooster characteristics; and very young roosters, if castrated and deprived of male hormones, lose their 'cockiness' and become feminized. In dogs, young female puppies if dosed with male hormones assume the male position in urinating (one hind leg raised, where female dogs otherwise squat). Also, in rats and guinea pigs, as well as poultry, individual animals who are aggressive and dominant over others can be made submissive by decreasing their male hormones and increasing their female hormones; or by the reverse process, submissive animals can be made aggressive and dominant.

Experiments such as those just mentioned have not, of course, been performed on human beings. However, certain diseases or defects which disturb and greatly change the balance of the sex hormones in either boys or girls can swerve their behaviour patterns from what is usual for their sex. Most pronounced are the feminizing effects of castration on boys *before puberty*. Castration in maturity, when the masculine physical and behaviour traits already have been set, produces only limited and gradual effects on behaviour. Nevertheless, it will also be noted that as men age, and their output of male hormones decreases, they become progressively less 'masculine' in behaviour, and very old men may behave not too differently from old women. As for females, what corresponds to castration – removal of the ovaries – before puberty, may produce only slight behaviour changes; and the changes may be even slighter, and only very gradual, if the operation is performed in maturity.

The *menopause*, also called the 'change of life', marks the natural end of the woman's reproductive, or possible further childbearing phase, although she may still be otherwise vigorous and healthy, and sometimes well under forty. While behaviour changes often accompany the menopause, and may result from the biological changes and transitions, the effects may be considerably intensified by the psychological state of the woman. As a rule, women who have previously been well balanced emotionally show little behaviour change during and after the menopause.

One also hears of *male* 'change of life'. But there is little to show that men have anything equivalent to the female menopause. There is no abrupt stoppage in men of reproductive capacity, but rather a gradual diminution which is part of the general ageing process. Any marked behaviour changes which might also occur in a man during his late forties or in his fifties are quite likely to be almost entirely psychological, the results of his feeling that he is 'losing his grip'.

Many of the biological sex abnormalities discussed in Chapter 13, such as defects or peculiarities of the sex organs, retarded sex development, premature sex development, etc., also obviously affect behaviour. While heredity may play a part in some of thse conditions, as explained, the effects on behaviour result largely from the way the individual, and the family or outsiders, regard the biological abnormalities.

How far the many significant psychological, social, and behaviour differences observable between little boys and girls are due to inborn factors, or to the way they are trained, cannot be easily determined. As parents have observed, little boys as a rule tend to be more restless, active, aggressive, destructive, and somewhat harder to manage. Little girls are usually more restrained, more self-sufficient and quieter in play, preferring dolls to mechanical toys; and after the age of two or three, they tend to be more aware of people, shyer, and perhaps more nervous (with more nail-biting and thumb-sucking) than boys. Also, as noted in Chapter 19, little girls show greater hand dexterity and independence in dressing themselves. At least some of these differences appearing in the first few years have been regarded as influenced by natural tendencies, because even among lower animals young males and females act differently in various ways. But undoubtedly, as childhood progresses, the ways in which boys and girls are reared would heavily accentuate and more strongly differentiate any of their inborn behaviour differences.

Almost everywhere in the world the traits linked with males and most admired in them are strength, virility, bravery, aggressiveness, dominance, enterprise, adventurousness, interest in outdoor activity and ability to *do* things (particularly of a mechanical nature). Linked with and most admired in females are interest and proficiency in domestic activities (cooking, sewing, homemaking, child-rearing), tenderness, affection, sentimentality, sensitivity, etc. These trait distinctions provide the basis of the 'M-F' tests devised by Professor Lewis M. Terman and others for measuring the relative degrees of masculinity and feminity shown by given individuals. But as indicated previously, there is much question as to the relationship between these test scores and the biological sex traits. One could argue that greater strength, aggressiveness, dominance, and bravery in a physical sense could be more naturally characteristic of men, as they are of males among other species (bulls, roosters, stags, etc.). And again, traits such as tenderness and domesticity might also develop more naturally among women through their childbearing, and child-rearing functions. Yet in a psychological sense there is no evidence at all that women cannot be and are not as brave, aggressive, enterprising, and venturesome as men. If they reveal these qualities less it could be much more because of social influences than of their gene workings.

So far in this chapter we have dealt with *sex* behaviour. Now we turn to *sexual* behaviour, which, as was previously explained, refers specifically to the impulses, feelings, and acts connected with the sex organs and sexual outlets. This is an enormous subject. We must limit ourselves to the possible hereditary aspects as they relate to individual differences in sexual behaviour, and to those types of behaviour which are markedly unusual and non-average, or 'abnormal'.

Socio-sexual development refers to a human being's sexual behaviour as it develops in relationship to other persons. In average individuals such sexual development proceeds through quite definite stages, as listed below; and it is when these stages are not properly experienced or completed that cause for concern, or suspicion of 'abnormality', may arise.

– In infancy and babyhood there is interest only in one's own sex organs and feelings. Individuals stopping at this stage are the *narcissists* who cannot show sexual feeling for anyone but themselves, and derive satisfaction only from their own bodies. Causes are probably psychological.

– In early childhood there is play with members of the opposite sex, but without conscious sex interest. Those who do not outgrow this stage remain undeveloped in their sexual feelings and responses, and very low in sex-drive. While again the causes may be psychological, sometimes they are traceable to deficiencies or defects in the sex glands and organs, which may or may not have a hereditary basis. (See Chapter 13, 'Sex Abnormalities'.)

– Ages six to ten (approximately): Interest only in those of one's own sex, and disinterest in or aversion to the opposite sex. Those remaining at this stage after puberty and into maturity may be in danger of developing into *homosexuals*. (See later discussion.)

– During adolescence there is increasingly marked interest in the opposite sex and an urge for sexual relationships, but with little discrimination and no desire for permanency. Those who do not pass beyond this stage may include, among males, the 'Don Juans' and among females, the 'nymphomaniacs' – persons constantly seeking new and frequent sexual partners because they lack mature sex feeling, and never can obtain full satisfaction with anyone. Psychoanalysts also regard many Don Juans as suffering from partial impotency, or fear of impotency, and many of the nymphomaniacs as being *frigid* women. Inherent factors, such as glandular deficiencies or nerve defects, may be involved in certain of the cases, but in most others the causes are chiefly or entirely psychological.

– Maturity brings selection (where there is opportunity to do so) of one individual of the opposite sex as a permanent mate, not only for sexual union, but for marriage and establishing a home, family, and social life. This is considered as the final – and socially approved – stage of sexual development in most civilizations. Whether it is also the 'natural' final stage, dictated by inherited impulses, would be difficult to prove. At any rate, achievement of this stage is the standard by which 'normal' adult sexual behaviour is judged in the United States and many other countries.

How do the actual sex lives of men and women conform to the standards apparently set for them? The voluminous and widely publicized reports on human sexual behaviour by the late Professor Alfred C. Kinsey and his associates sought to show this by presenting detailed facts on the sex lives of more than fifteen thousand males and females. However, since the Kinsey studies have so far been concerned mainly with what human sexual behaviour *is*, rather than what *causes* it, there is very little evidence in the reports that bears directly on hereditary aspects of human sexual behaviour, and where such evidence is offered, there is question as to whether it can yet be accepted as scientific proof. Of chief interest here are the following Kinsey observations and conclusions, briefly summarized:

– The most important biologic factors affecting human sexual behaviour are the hereditary forces that account for the differences between male and female. Within either sex, heredity must also account for some of the variation in sensory structures and mechanisms which affect sexual responses and performance.

– Males begin their active sexual lives much earlier than

females and reach their peak of sexual potency and expression at about age seventeen, whereas with females the sexual peak does not come until almost age thirty.

– The total lifetime sexual performance of an average male is vastly greater than that of the female, but some females are capable of enormously more sexual performance than males.

– Males by nature are much more stimulated sexually through psychological influences than are females, are much more inclined to promiscuity and require far more sexual expression.

– Many cases of *frigidity* in women may be due to the fact that they were 'never equipped to respond erotically'; and among males, some cases of impotency or low sex-drive may also be the result of inherent factors.

– No type of sexual behaviour in human beings can be considered 'abnormal' or 'unnatural', and if it were not for training to the contrary, almost every person would indulge in almost every type of sexual behaviour.

(With respect to all of the foregoing statements, it must again be stressed that they cannot be accepted as established facts, for, although considered valid by some authorities, they have been challenged by others. Moreover, Dr Kinsey himself had presented many of his findings as 'tentative', pending further research.)

Homosexuality (first with respect to males) has many puzzling and debatable aspects, particularly as related to the *overt* homosexuals – those who consistently and preferably turn for their sexual relationships to their own sex and who have many distinctive and easily recognizable mannerisms, 'feminine' or otherwise. (Some overt homosexuals, however, are outwardly extremely masculine in appearance and actions.) The incidence of homosexuality is uncertain. In the sample of males who volunteered for the Kinsey interviews, 13 per cent were classed as 'predominantly homosexual', and 4 per cent as exclusively so; but there is strong suspicion that the 'Kinsey' males included disproportionate numbers of the non-average. Various other studies indicate that the true incidence of the more overt male homosexuals in the United States and elsewhere may approach 3 per cent.

It is quite likely that different types and degrees of homosexuality may arise through different factors, psychological, social, and biological. While most authorities stress the psychological influences, there is also some possibility of inborn quirks in homosexuality of the more overt types. As reasons: (1) Overt homosexuals have appeared among human beings throughout history and in the most diverse environments. (2) Many homosexuals everywhere, whether in the most primitive or the most civilized societies, show remarkable similarities in movements, mannerisms, vocal inflexions, and various other behaviour traits. (3) They often seem to arise spontaneously, with tendencies shown in childhood, and with no conditioning factors that can explain them. (4) Studies of *twins*, by Dr Franz J. Kallmann and others, show that in the great majority of cases where one of a pair of identical twins was homosexual, so was the other, but that this was not true of fraternal twins; and that 35 per cent of the twin homosexuals came from families where the trait had appeared in other members.

A few scientists have maintained that homosexuals of the extreme 'invert' type (with feminine physical traits) may represent an in-between sex. In certain lower species one does find individuals in whom the sex chromosomes are out of balance, so that they are neither completely male nor completely female. But there is no proof that this happens in human beings, or if it does, that it would change the direction of a person's sex interests from the opposite sex towards his or her own sex. Another theory is that overt male homosexuals tend to be deficient in male sex hormones. But tests have not proved this to be so as a rule, nor have hormonal treatments been found to change homosexual impulses.

Whether or not inborn tendencies or susceptibilities are involved in homosexuality, there is considerable evidence that specific environmental factors can do much to turn a person towards this behaviour. Most often held responsible for male homosexuality are neurotic, sexually frustrated, dominant or clinging mothers, who seek to raise their boys as girls, and implant in them fear or distaste of opposite-sex relationships. However, there are many cases where such influences are lacking, and where it would be highly unfair to blame the parent. In any case, if the homosexually inclined individual is still young, or in an indecisive stage, there is a good chance of conditioning him towards normalcy. But in an adult, once the homosexual pattern has been strongly set, there is at present little evidence that it can be changed either by medical or psychological treatment.

The problem of *female homosexuality* is not as serious as that of male homosexuality because the incidence is much lower (probably under 1 per cent), it is much less on the surface, and its social effects are not as harmful. For one thing, the greater need and desire of women to marry and have children acts to suppress any homosexual tendencies in them more than in males. Otherwise most of the basic facts given for male homosexuality apply to the corresponding behaviour in the female. Thus, while some female homosexuals are masculine in outward appearance and behaviour, many others are completely feminine in all respects save their sexual inclinations (although they may have relationships with males as well as females). Again, some female homosexuals appear to be products solely of warped emotional or psychological conditioning, but others seem to have started with strong inner tendencies towards abnormal sexual behaviour, which may or may not have had a biological basis. Finally, as with males, the chance for conditioning a homosexually inclined female towards normalcy depends largely on whether she is in the young and/or indecisive stage, or is adult and has already been strongly set in the homosexual pattern.

CHAPTER TWENTY-FIVE

HUMAN EVOLUTION

TO UNDERSTAND HOW human beings originated on this earth, one must have some idea of how life of any kind first began and how it led to the development of all the countless types and forms of other living things. The process by which scientists believe this was achieved is called *evolution*. When people use this term they are apt to think of Charles Darwin, for it was his theories of evolution, published in 1859, which revised all previous concepts. What caused the most controversy and opposition was Darwin's contention that the different creatures were not created suddenly, at the same time, and in their existing forms, but developed step by step, over very long periods, from other and simpler types; and, specifically, that *human beings* had also developed from lower forms of animals.

To many persons, the Darwinian theories may have seemed a direct contradiction of the Biblical account of Creation as having taken place in six 'days', and of man in one 'day'. But others have realized that there actually need be no real conflict on this point if one interprets the Biblical 'days' of Creation as meaning *stages* of indefinite length. By this definition modern science holds very closely in most respects to the Biblical concept of the successive stages of Creation: (1) The earth being 'without form, and void', then being shaped into a mass covered by water, with 'light' – the heat and energy from the sun – a first essential in all that was to take place; (2) land rising from beneath the waters, forming continents and islands surrounded by oceans; (3) the growth of vegetation; (4) changes in climate, environments, and food conditions; (5) the creation and existence of the simplest creatures, gradually developing into fish, reptiles, fowl, and mammals; (6) finally the evolution (or creation) of man. If scientists think of this as happening not in a 'week', but in vast stretches of time – three billion years or more – and in endlessly remarkable ways, it can only add to the wonder of Creation.

In explaining evolution, scientists begin with the assumption that the first living thing was a single cell consisting of a *single gene* housed in a blob of the life-stuff, protoplasm. (This cell may have come from a simpler, virus-like cell, in between living and non-living.) Endowed with the property of life and reproduction, the first gene cell could multiply itself endlessly. Very soon, among the millions of separate offspring cells, *mutations* – changes in genes – began to take place, making some different from the others. As mutations increased, different genes began hooking up into chains to form chromosomes. And with each change in the types, numbers, and varieties of genes and chromosomes, there also were changes in the types and complexities of the cell formations, and of the creatures they produced. Not least important was the creation of *two sexes*. At the beginning creatures reproduced by dividing themselves, so hereditary changes from one generation to another were limited. But when mutations produced sex genes, then sex chromosomes, and thus individuals of two sexes, this greatly extended the possibility of making new combinations of genes with each mating and speeding up evolutionary changes.

Altogether, in a rough way the process of evolution in living things was not too unlike that which came later in the evolution of man-made machines. From the first crude tools fashioned by man – chipped rocks – there evolved hand axes, spears, arrows, knives, needles, and tools and devices of innumerable kinds. From the first simple wheel there evolved vehicles and machinery growing ever more complex, until, with the discovery of engines, there came automobiles and huge aeroplanes. Tree-trunk canoes to battleships, windmills to giant power plants, bullets to atomic bombs – all of these were the results of countless successive inventive mutations. So, too, all the varieties of living and growing things in our world today are the products of vastly more numerous and complex *genetic* mutations. Just to produce the human eye alone, for instance, must have required thousands of mutations over millions of years.

Aiding continuously in the processes of evolution has been the fact that as different mutations popped up, if they served some useful purpose or offered an advantage to a creature at a given time they survived. But where mutations produced a defect or disadvantage (true in the great majority of cases) the creatures died off. In this process of 'selecting out' the good mutations and weeding out the bad ones, *environment* was always a factor. Each type or change of climate, food supply, natural hazard, enemy, disease, or other condition demanded something special in an animal for survival and development. Different mutations answered these needs, in the forms of particular kinds of bodies, feathers, furs, skins, claws, teeth, colouring, internal organs, breathing apparatus, sensory equipment (eyes, ears, sense of smell), and not least, *brains*, as well as many other details.

But if the right mutations didn't come along, species of creatures could often also survive and thrive by *moving* to some new environments, or being moved there by the winds, water, earth upheavals, or climatic changes. Either way, groups of creatures originally of similar types spread out and became *segregated* from one another. And again, over new long periods of time, in each group new mutations kept appearing, which, in their different environments, were selected out and adapted differently, making the isolated groups increasingly different from one another. These, plus other factors (including crossbreeding and various chance elements), can account for the innumerable kinds of birds, fishes, mammals, and other animals, and the varieties of each species that are peculiar to given regions and localities the world over.

The erroneous old theory that evolution proceeded because traits *acquired* by animals, through experiences and habits, were or could be inherited by their offspring, was briefly discussed in Chapter 2. Here are a few more points. The most questionable part of the theory is that what an animal needed or wanted – or no longer needed or wanted – could *cause* a particular mutation to take place. If giraffes had to keep stretching their necks to eat high up on trees, they would somehow cause their offspring to be born with longer and longer necks; or if animals stopped using some part of their body, their genes would stop providing it. But there is just no way of explaining *how* this could occur. If an animal kept stretching its neck, how could that shake up or change its 'neck' genes so as to put more stretch in their workings? If a red bird was too easily spotted by enemies in green trees, how could that *make* its 'colour' genes begin to produce green feathers? Obviously this is impossible. The probable fact, as already indicated, is that in each species mutations of every conceivable kind kept coming along purely through chance (as they still do, which can be seen by observing flies, mice, and other creatures in laboratories). With the desirable mutations being retained, the bad ones eliminated, for generation after generation, as one useful mutation was added to another, this could conceivably have produced in sufficient time any type of creature, or the particular inherited traits in all the creatures existing today.

An old question is 'Which came first, the chicken or the egg?' The facts as science now gives them clearly answer that the *egg* came first. By the old acquired-characteristic theories it would have been the chicken. That is, one would start with a type of bird which, through gradual changes in habits and environments, presumably turned into a chicken, which *then* produced the characteristic chicken egg. But modern genetics holds that mutations kept producing different kinds of genes in eggs of a bird species, which in time caused these *eggs* to produce chickens. As applied to persons and eggs, for instance, a blue-eyed baby does not result because its parents were blue-eyed persons (often they are dark-eyed), but because the *egg* from which the baby came carried blue-eye genes. Originally it is possible that there were no human blue-eye genes and that one suddenly arose through mutation. Thus again it was not the blue-eyed person, but the blue-eyed *egg* which came first.

The acquired characteristics were revived some years ago by

a group of Soviet plant breeders, headed by Trofim Lysenko, who also attacked various other principles of modern genetics. The attack, starting in the 1930's, led to the exiling of Russia's top geneticist, Vavilov, to Siberia (where he died in 1942), and the forced recantation of their scientific beliefs by many other Russian geneticists after the Soviet Central Committee, in 1948, proclaimed the Lysenko theories as the only 'correct and acceptable' ones. Lysenko's claims went farthest when he reported in 1949 that he had succeeded in *turning wheat into rye* by environmental changes – which, to geneticists, would seem as likely as causing cats to give birth to puppies by changing their diet and living conditions. However, by 1954, Soviet scientists were beginning to challenge Lysenko on his theories, although he was apparently still strong in his official position.

Many believe that Lysenko's rise to power with Soviet political leaders came in part because of his success as a practical plant breeder, and in part because his claims offered support to the Marxist theories of the all-importance of environment. What seemed to have been overlooked was that if good environment could cause an improvement in the *heredity* of plants (or human beings), *bad environment* could cause a deterioration in heredity. And on that basis, the Russian people, long exposed to very bad environments, would have developed inferior hereditary traits – which, of course, is completely contrary to what modern genetics has established.

The scientific story of human evolution begins perhaps 50,000,000 years ago. By that time the earth was teeming with creatures of every kind. Among them were some now called 'primates', who were smarter and nimbler than other animals. In succeeding millions of years innumerable mutations produced different types and branches of the primate family. Some were the monkeys – lemurs, spider monkeys, macaques, baboons. From the more intelligent branches came the great apes – the gibbon, orangutan, chimpanzee, and gorilla. And finally, from another *separate* branch, and 'twigs' of this branch, there began to develop species of the brainiest of all creatures – *man*. In other words, *human beings did not descend from apes*, but both apes and men came from the same primate tree. So while we and the apes of today have common ancestors, our relationship is millions of years apart, and the best any ape can claim is that he and we are very, very distant cousins.

With all the manifold differences, we nevertheless recognize that monkeys and apes are far more like us than are any other animals. That is why we are so fascinated watching them in zoos or on television, and why we call people we like 'little monkeys', and those we don't, 'apes', or 'gorillas'. From the scientific standpoint, the fact that human beings belong to the same primate family as do monkeys and apes is proved in a great many ways: by unique similarities in their skulls, bones, teeth, eyes, hands and feet, and internal organs; by menstruation in their females (the only lower animals among whom this occurs); by closely similar periods of gestation (eight months for apes); by late onset of puberty (age nine or ten for apes); and, most recently discovered and perhaps most important, by *blood types* (those in apes being almost exactly like the A, B, O, Rh, and other blood groups in humans). The one tremendous difference, though, is in *brains*. Mainly it was the series of additional brain mutations on the human branch of the primate tree (plus improvements in the hands and skeletal framework) that carried men so far beyond all other creatures, and left the apes and monkeys almost back where they were millions of years ago.

Between the time that the man family began to evolve, far in the dimmest past, and the point where anything like true human beings appeared, there were a great many 'experimental models' of ape-men, part-men, half-men, and near-men, who died out or were killed off as improved types of man came along. We know of those man-types, fairly late in the procession (a million years or so ago), only through a scant few of their skulls and bones which have been found. These earliest man-creatures have been named after the places where relics were dug up: the 'South African Ape-Man' (or 'Man-Ape'), the 'Java Man', the 'Pekin Man', the 'Heidelberg Man', the 'Swanscombe Man', etc. (The 'Piltdown Man', once classed

THE EVOLUTION OF APES AND MAN

(ACCORDING TO CURRENT THEORIES)

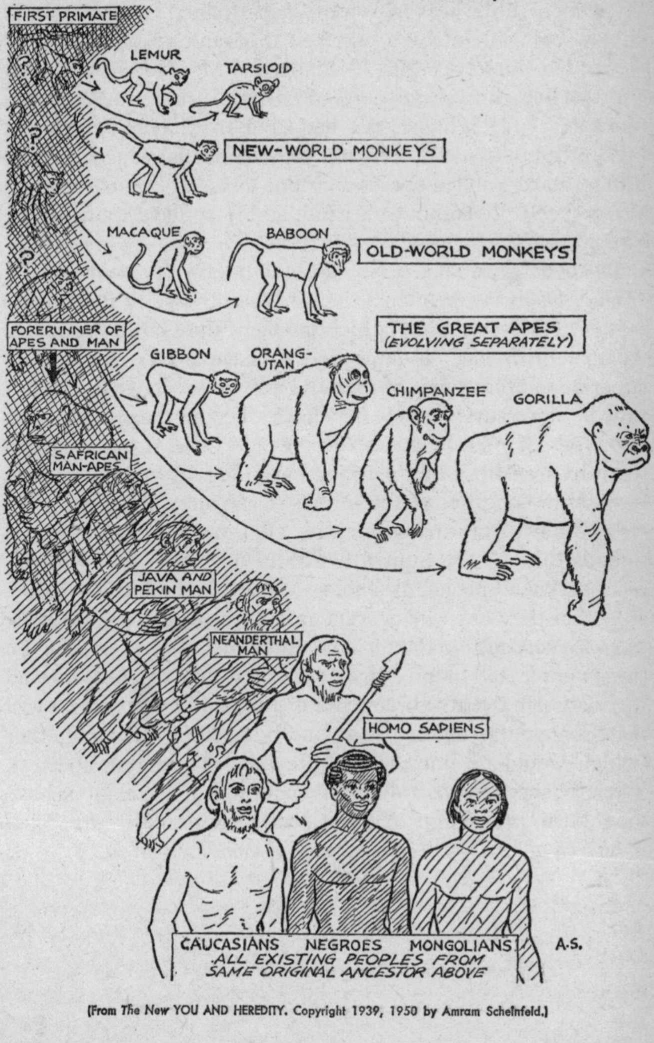
FIRST PRIMATE
LEMUR
TARSIOID
NEW-WORLD MONKEYS
MACAQUE
BABOON
OLD-WORLD MONKEYS
FORERUNNER OF APES AND MAN
THE GREAT APES (EVOLVING SEPARATELY)
GIBBON
ORANG-UTAN
CHIMPANZEE
GORILLA
S. AFRICAN MAN-APES
JAVA AND PEKIN MAN
NEANDERTHAL MAN
HOMO SAPIENS
CAUCASIANS NEGROES MONGOLIANS
ALL EXISTING PEOPLES FROM SAME ORIGINAL ANCESTOR ABOVE
A.S.

(From *The New* YOU AND HEREDITY. Copyright 1939, 1950 by Amram Scheinfeld.)

among these ancients, was proved in 1953 to have been a hoax whose bones had been faked and planted in England.) All of these were still heavy-browed, half-brained, stooped, and clumsy beings. But by a hundred thousand years ago a man almost like ourselves – the 'Neanderthal Man' – had appeared and was living in various parts of Africa, Europe, and Asia. He was about 5 feet 3 inches tall, had a big brow, a heavy jaw, and big teeth, but a good brain and capable hands, which enabled him to make wooden spears and flint tools, and to use fire. He also respectfully laid out his dead, and must have shown other human traits.

By about 50,000 B.C. a New Man of our own present species, *Homo sapiens* ('wise man'), had evolved, possibly first in the region of Mesopotamia (which is where the Garden of Eden, Adam's birthplace, is supposed to have been). He was so superior to other types of men in brain power and skill that in time he alone survived. He may have killed off the cruder existing types of men (such as the Neanderthalers), or absorbed them by breeding; or they may have died off because of new diseases or conditions. About that we can only guess. But what we do know, from many scientific studies, tests, and observations is this: all the human beings in the world today, of all races and in all places, are biologically and genetically so much alike that they must be descendants of the same original stock of *Homo sapiens*. No matter how different they may seem to be (for example, tall blond Nordics and African Pygmies), they all carry similar twenty-three pairs of human chromosomes with matching genes, and can mate and be fertile with one another (which would be impossible were they of different species). Thus, science now corroborates what most great religions have long been preaching: *Human beings of all races are equal 'Children of God', descended from the same First Man.*

CHAPTER TWENTY-SIX

THE HUMAN RACES, I: PHYSICAL DIFFERENCES

KNOWING THAT ALL human beings are of exactly the same species, descended from the same original Man, how explain the many differences among them in features, colouring, and other physical traits, as well as in behaviour, culture, and achievement? For the answer we return to the very beginnings of our species – *Homo sapiens*, about 50,000 years ago, and trace the story of racial differentiation as science now sees it.

Starting with a single fruitful couple (Adam and Eve, if you wish), favourable conditions could have resulted in close to a million descendants in less than a thousand years. But in those early periods, with no fixed habitats, large groups would not have held together. So, moving wherever climate and the search for food led them, bands of people would have drifted apart, losing contact with one another, and spreading eventually to all habitable places of the earth. In time, then, these isolated human groups, multiplying and becoming fixed in different environments for thousands of years, would have developed various special hereditary characteristics through the continuing processes of evolution. We noted in the last chapter how *selection* and *adaptation* of gene changes as they came along in different environments, plus chance factors, could produce many varieties of birds or other animals of each species. The same factors could just as easily produce the many physical differences among human racial groups. (Their cultural and behaviour differences, however, must be explained in other ways, to be dealt with later.)

The word 'race' can be applied only loosely to human beings because there are no large human groups all of whose members are completely different in any one trait from all those of other racial groups. We can make racial distinctions only with respect to *average* differences in a given number of inherited traits, to the extent that they occur in markedly different proportions in different groups. On this basis most scientists classify all human beings into four primary, or main races (with the popular names given in parentheses):

1. *Caucasoid* (or 'white') race, developing and concentrated largely in Europe, Asia Minor, India, and parts of North Africa. It is not known whether the white race was the first to develop; many authorities think the first members of *Homo sapiens* were dark, with Negroid features.

2. *Negroid* ('black') race, developing and concentrated largely in Africa, later spreading to some adjoining regions and then also being carried to the Americas and the West Indies.

3. *Mongoloid* ('yellow', or 'yellow-brown') race, developing and concentrated mainly in Asia, and islands or regions adjoining it. Mongoloids are considered 'younger' in evolutionary origin than either the whites or the Negroes.

4. *Australoid* race, comprising primitive peoples in and around Australia, with origins not too certain, but believed to stem from a very early mixture of Negroid and Mongoloid, and also some Caucasoid stocks.

The classifications by skin colour, it should be kept in mind, are very questionable. As was pointed out in Chapter 8, people of all races have the same skin pigments, though in different proportions. 'Whites', for instance, are clearly not 'white'-skinned. (They would look ghastly if they were.) What they themselves call their 'flesh colour', is actually pinkish-brown, as shown by the face powder or adhesive finger bandages they use. Further, many whites, such as swarthy Latins and Arabs, are very dark, and some in India have skins much blacker than many Negroes. Nor is 'black' a correct term for many Negroid peoples who, without any mixture of white genes, have light-brown skins. So, too, the Mongoloids have a considerable range of skin colours, and while to some eyes their skins might seem to have a slight yellowish cast, this is only a variation of the basic human brown colour.

An old, false theory is that people of some races can be proved to be less human than others because their features are more apelike. Although comparisons on this point have little meaning, it can easily be shown that persons of each race have some features that are farthest from the ape form and some closest to it. For instance, the kinky hair of Negroes is less apelike than the straight or wavy hair of whites, and the sparse body hair of Negroes and Chinese is less apelike than the hairiness of whites. The full lips of Negroes put them farther away from the thin-lipped apes than are whites. This no more proves that whites are most apelike than broad noses of Negroes prove Negroes are, or Eskimos' thin noses prove they're least so.

Each main race has (and had originally or developed in time) various subgroups, some being offshoots from the main race, and others blends with other races. Some examples:

– *American Indians and Eskimos.* These are Mongoloid offshoots, who, starting perhaps 25,000 years ago, began crossing over from Asia by way of a narrow strip of land then connecting Siberia with Alaska. The Mongols who formed or developed into the Eskimos and the various Indian tribes of North, Central, and South America (including the Incas and Aztecs), did not come all at once, but separately, at long intervals, and where they show marked differences were probably already different Mongolian subgroups when they started out from Asia.

– *The Negroes.* A common error is to think of Negroes in Africa (or in the United States) as all of one racial stock. Actually, they are of many racial subgroups, with differences going back thousands of years and greater than are found among whites. Some of the most striking differences are those between the tall, spindly, seven-foot Watusis of East Africa and the stocky Pygmies of the Congo, while the Bushmen-Hottentots of South Africa are so different in many respects from other Negroids that some anthropologists believe they constitute a separate race. Other African Negroes, the Zulus (Bantus), Sudanese, etc., also have distinctive physical traits.

Thus, since American Negroes, whose ancestors were taken from many parts of Africa, are mixtures of many Negroid strains, plus some amounts of Indian and white genes, they might be considered in the mass as a new Negro subrace, genetically different from all other Negro subraces.

– *The Japanese.* While a subgroup of the Mongoloids, as are also the Chinese, the Japanese are distinct in various racial respects from other Mongols. One fact is their part-white ancestry through the Ainus, a short, hairy, Caucasoid people who may once have been quite prevalent from Russia to northern Asia, and primitive remnants of whom still live in northern Japanese islands. Also mixed in with the Japanese strain are genes from various Pacific islanders.

When peoples are distinguished from one another less by inherited factors than by differences in culture, history, and nationality, they are referred to as *ethnic groups.** 'Ethnic' is often confused with 'racial' (as are environmental traits with hereditary traits), especially as applied to European peoples. Thus, mistaken references often are made to the 'Nordic', 'Baltic', 'Alpine', and 'Mediterranean' 'races', when they actually are ethnic groups with few clear-cut genetic differences among them. This is seen when we look into the origins of Europeans and find they are all highly mixed peoples, not at all 'pure' whites, but having both Mongoloid genes, brought in through early Hun and African invasions, and also some Negro genes brought in at various other times. Here are some of the mixtures that went into the principal European nationalities:

English: Ancient Celts, Romans (and mixed Mediterraneans including North Africans), Anglo-Saxons, Danish Vikings, Normans, Germans.

* Some anthropologists now maintain that the term 'ethnic groups' should apply even to the largest divisions of mankind, and that the word 'race' should be abandoned entirely. The contention is that no human groups are so distinct from one another biologically that they can be regarded as belonging to different races. Other anthropologists dispute this and maintain that the broad classification of human beings into races is still valid.

Irish: Ancient Picts, ancient peoples from France, Denmark, the Rhine (Celts) and Spain, Scandinavians, Normans, etc.

Germans: Unknown primitive tribes, ancient Celts, Romans, Huns, Slavs, Franks and Saxons, Vikings, Huguenots.

Norwegians and Swedes: Early Germanic tribes (through Denmark), Finns, Teutons, Lapps.

French: North Africans, North Italians, Celts (Gauls), Romans, Germanic tribes, Huns, Norsemen, English.

Italians: Ancient Sabines, Phoenicians, Etruscans, Greeks, Gauls, Goths, Lombards, Normans, German–Swabians, French.

Spanish: Iberians (from North Africa), Celts, Greeks, Carthaginians, Romans (Visigoths), Germanic peoples, Moors.

Russians: Finns, early Germanic tribes, Huns, Slavs, Turk-Tartaric peoples, Tartars, Vikings, Germans.

Hungarians: Celts, Romans, Vandals, Germanic Lombards and Goths, Huns and Avars, Slavs, Italians, French, Germans, Tartars, Turks.

Within or among the human groups there are certain large clusters of people who are a sort of cross between ethnic and racial: that is, while originally of mixed stocks, they have held together for a long enough time, like large family groups, to develop various average hereditary similarities as well as common religious and cultural traits. To these subgroups some anthropologists believe the term 'kith' might be applied. Thus, the Jews, Irish, Scots, and Roumanians are considered examples of kiths.

That the Jews definitely do not constitute a racial group, but can be described more as a kith, is clearly shown by those collected in Israel today. The marked differences in physical appearance, features, and colouring among the various groups – Yemenite, Moroccan, Polish, Russian, Roumanian, German, Spanish, Italian, Syrian, English, and American Jews – not only reflect the different countries and environments from which they came, but also are proof that they are *genetically* different in various ways. Explaining this is the fact that continually through their wanderings they have absorbed genes of other peoples among whom they have lived (through converts to their religion, intermarriages, sometimes rape of their women, etc.).

It is true that on the average some genetic characteristics are more common among Jews than non-Jews. But in any Jewish population a very large proportion of the individuals can in no sense be identified as Jewish by any physical traits, and this proportion is growing, especially in new generations of Jews in the United States and other countries, as their training and living conditions become like those of other groups. (Supposed distinguishing features of Americans of Irish, Scots, and other kiths are also becoming less and less marked in the newer generations.) Even in Israel visitors are struck by the fact that so many of the younger, native-born Jews ('Sabras'), reared and working in the Israeli farming communities, look so non-Jewish by former stereotyped ideas.

As previously indicated, many of the main differences among races in colouring, features, and even body types, may well have evolved because they served some useful purpose in their original environments. As with lower animals, in early human history it may have been a matter of life and death whether individuals and groups had this or that type of physical equipment to cope with existing conditions. (Even in the United States today many people move from North to South, or vice versa, or from some other region to another, because they 'can't stand the climate' where they are.) Thus, it is not mere coincidence that the darkest-skinned, blackest-eyed peoples arose and were long concentrated in the hottest climates (and for the most part still live there), while the lightest-skinned and lightest-eyed peoples developed and live in the more temperate regions. Although great improvements in housing, heating, refrigeration, clothing, and drugs, and in industrial devices, have reduced the early importance of inherited race differences in various environments, they still have their usefulness, or may prove to be more useful than we have believed. Various recent scientific findings bear on these points.

Negroes (and dark-skinned whites, such as those in India, the Arab countries, and North Africa) are best protected against the hot (ultraviolet) rays of the sun because of the heavier underlying deposit of melanin pigment particles in their skins (Chapter 8). Moreover, Negroes with the heaviest pigmentation have been found less likely than whites to develop skin cancer in the tropics; also, because Negro skin has an extra outer protecting layer, it is more resistant to germs and infections in hot, damp tropical climates, and to scratches in the jungles. Whites, on the other hand, have an advantage in cooler climates because their more lightly pigmented skins permit a maximum of the beneficial vitamin D irradiation from the sun. (The in-between, yellow-brown skin of the Mongolians or bronzed skin of American Indians may also offer some advantages in their native environments, but this has not been established.) Again, the heavily pigmented Negro eyes, with added pigment inside the retina and in the eyelids, are better adapted than white eyes to the glaring tropics.

The broader nostrils of the Negroes may permit better breathing in hot, moist climates, whereas in cool regions the smaller, narrower white nostrils are better adapted to warming up cold air before it enters the lungs. The Eskimos, it may be noted, have among the narrowest of noses. But also, some authorities believe, Eskimos have been aided in adapting to Arctic cold by their fatty eyelids and underlayers of other facial as well as body fat, and by their stocky figures and stubby limbs and hands which do not permit as much heat evaporation as do long, thin legs. Contrariwise, the spindly legs, long, thin hands, and lanky figures of many Negroes are better adapted to heat evaporation in hot climates. In the matter of leg structure, some authorities believe that the particular formation and musculature of the legs of some strains of Negroes may be assets in running ability, and may partly explain the upsurge of Negro champions in track and racing events, once they have had the chance to train and compete. It is also possible that the tightly curled or kinky Negroid hair may permit better scalp ventilation in the tropics.

In addition to the race differences mentioned there are others, some brought to light only recently (such as the blood types), whose usefulness or adaptive value remains uncertain or unknown. The Mongolian skin fold at the eye corner, some authorities believe, may help in protecting the eyes from the glare of the sun (or, with Eskimos, from ice and snow glare) by narrowing the slits through which the eyes are exposed. However, no good guesses have been made as to why Mongolians have such scant facial and body hair, or thick, black straight hair. Or why Negroes have thick lips. Or, among whites, what practical advantage or disadvantage there may be in straight hair, or wavy or curly, or brown, red, or blond hair. Or why women of some racial groups have much larger breasts, or different breast shapes, or more heavily padded buttocks, than others. Or why head shapes differ on the average among races. Many of these differences may be merely the results of Nature's decorative whims, unrelated to usefulness; or they may prove to have once had practical value, in given environments, or to be related to some internal chemical or functional traits that still have meaning.

Blood-group differences have now become perhaps the most important anthropological criteria for classifying human groups and tracing their origins. Just as individuals and families differ in their blood types (A, B, O, or the Rh groups, or M-N types, discussed in Chapter 15), there are blood-type differences – though only in *average* incidences – among racial and ethnic groups. These differences have nothing to do with blood 'quality' or 'strength', but are of interest to anthropologists because of the clues they offer in tracing the origins and relationships of racial and ethnic groups, and may also be useful legally in disputed paternity cases. The layman, however, can be only mildly interested in such facts as that the O blood type occurs in 46 per cent of the English, 50 per cent of the Spaniards, 29 per cent of the Japanese, 61 per cent of the Ethiopians and in almost 100 per cent of some pure American

Indian tribes; that blood type B is most common among Asiatics and less frequent among Europeans; that blood type A ranges from up to 50 per cent among Europeans to 15 per cent among Filipinos; or that the M and N types have such and such racial incidences. With respect to whites and Negroes, it has now been found that in addition to the much lower Rh-negative incidence among Negroes, a majority of them carry an Rh blood-group antigen called V, inherited as a dominant, whereas this is present in hardly 1 in 100 whites.

Disease differences among races and ethnic groups are also of great interest. But because living conditions, diets, hygiene, and other factors may vary greatly among racial and ethnic groups, it is often hard to tell whether or not heredity plays any important part in the different incidences of given diseases among them. We mentioned this with respect to Americans of different stocks. However, it was noted in the disease chapters that *Cooley's anaemia* is largely confined to Mediterranean whites, and *sicklaemia* to Negroes. Also, that *colour blindness* is twice as common among whites as among Negroes. Certain very rare diseases and defects have been found confined largely to small groups within one race or another, which is not surprising if the conditions arose through unusual mutations in comparatively recent times. Again, it is possible that some racial groups, through evolutionary changes, have developed special resistance to certain infectious diseases peculiar to their original environments, and are more susceptible to diseases of other environments. But on the whole, virtually all types of inherited diseases and defects are found among all racial groups, and where conditions are approximately the same, the major diseases (cancer, heart afflictions, diabetes, etc.) appear in much the same proportions.

Among other biological race differences are these: in tasting the PTC chemical, the incidence of tasters has been reported as 96 per cent among African Negroes, 94 per cent among Chinese, 70 per cent among American whites, and 63 per cent among Arabs. In *body chemistry*, certain differences have been reported between Chinese and European whites in normal excretions of amino acids (as shown through urinalyses), these differences being attributed not to diet but to inherited factors. In *fingerprints*, there are race differences in the relative incidences of whorls, loops, and arch. Whorls, for instance, are found in 25 per cent of the English, 45 per cent of Japanese, and 30 per cent of Jamaican Negroes.

CHAPTER TWENTY-SEVEN

THE HUMAN RACES, II: QUALITIES

OF ALL THE FACTS dealt with in this book, what many persons may find hardest to accept is this: that no race, ethnic group, or nationality (and specifically, their own) can be proved *better by heredity* in character or quality than any other. This statement strikes at deep-rooted conceits and prejudices that have caused countless bloody conflicts, that have brought death or suffering to untold millions of people, and that have been used to justify the enslavement or subjugation of some groups by other groups – not only in the past but in our own time, and at this moment. Fortunately, there is a growing realization that if mankind is to have a happier and more peaceful future, the peoples of the world must root out their old racial biases and adjust to the truths about themselves which science has been revealing. The most important of these truths we will try to present here.

The term 'racial stereotype' is applied to particular traits of temperament popularly associated with specific racial or ethnic groups: The English, 'cool, reserved'; Germans, 'militaristic, systematic'; Latins, 'excitable'; Irish, 'pugnacious'; Swedes, 'stolid'; Negroes, 'childlike, uninhibited'; Chinese, 'inscrutable'; Japanese, 'sly'; etc. Whatever limited truth there may be in these stereotypes in any general sense, it is certain that they do not apply to a great many individuals of each racial group, and in all probability have no hereditary basis. On the contrary, there is every likelihood that these group traits are purely the products of environment, habits, and training. This is clearly indicated in the United States by the fact that in a comparatively short time descendants of all races and nationalities have shed most of their supposed ancestral traits and taken on common characteristics of personality and temperament which peoples of other countries quickly identify as 'American'.

(A significant story in reverse, of how an American who had been adopted as a baby by a Chinese family and reared by them in China until age twenty, had thus developed many characteristic 'Chinese' traits, is told in the author's book, '*The New* You and Heredity'.)

The question of whether there are any racial differences in minds, or in types or degrees of capacity for various tasks, cannot be answered precisely, first, because environments are and have been so different for people of different groups; and second (as noted in Chapter 19), there are as yet no scientific tests by which their relative *inherited* mental capacities can be accurately determined. Theoretically it is possible that certain types of achievement genes were at a given period, or may even now be, concentrated more heavily in one racial group than another. But the belief that any racial group is unique with respect to the genes for talent, skill, or achievement as a whole is refuted by history, past and present.

During the thousands of years of man's cultural evolution, there has been virtually no racial group which at one time or another has not contributed greatly to progress in invention, industry, art, religion, science, social organization, and other fields. Changing places at the head of the historical procession of conquerors and cultural leaders have been Semites, Mongols, Egyptians, Greeks, Romans, Turks, Moors, and so on. And repeatedly, those out in front at one period fell behind later, and peoples who had long been backward or stagnant suddenly forged ahead of others. Even the so-called 'primitives' in the heart of Africa had (as they still have) highly organized political and social systems and had created intricate and beautiful works of art, far back at a time when many European peoples were much less advanced. Most recently we have seen the Japanese, Chinese, Hawaiians, Filipinos, and many other groups in Asia, and also Africa, prove within a generation or two that they could brush aside supposed inborn shortcomings and master the most complex modern technical know-how in short order. Similarly, wherever training and opportunities of peoples of any kind have begun to be equalized, their achievements, too, have approached more and more the same levels.

The belief that one racial group is by *inheritance* 'superior' in 'blood' and character, and destined by nature to dominate 'inferior' races, dates back actually no more than a century or two. Among ancient peoples there was no such race consciousness or prejudice. Kings would marry princesses of any other races, and Caesar hardly felt superior to Cleopatra, nor Solomon to the dark Queen of Sheba. Divisions among ancient peoples were tribal or political rather than racial. For instance, the Biblical Hebrews thought of themselves as a 'chosen people' mainly in the cultural and religious sense, and did not regard alien peoples as biologically inferior, nor ban intermarriage with those of other racial stocks who adopted their religion. Nor is there any evidence of any inborn or 'instinctive' antagonism between racial groups. On the contrary, science has shown that people have to be *taught* to hate and look down on persons of other races, and that without this training white children, for instance, would no more shun black or yellow children than white birds, cats, or dogs shun those of other colours. As it happens, racial antagonism in recent times has stemmed mainly from whites. When African Negroes and American Indians first met whites they were very friendly; even today, race prejudices refer chiefly to the attitudes of whites towards those of other races.

An astounding and appalling fact is that at a time when myths about race had been exploded by modern science, racial fanaticism reached its most dreadful extreme in one of the presumably most advanced countries, Germany. Millions of people died, and millions more suffered horribly, before Hitler's reign of terror ended. That this was due purely to a psychological sickness in a warped environment is clear today, for there is no question that the German people are not *by heredity* any more cruel, militaristic, or intolerant than others. But unfortunately it is not all past history, because the poisons of racial prejudice engendered by the Nazis have by no means been eradicated, and their false concepts continue to do harm.

We have already shown that the basic Nazi ideas – that the Germans constituted a race of 'superior' blood – were scientifically preposterous, since the Germans were (to cite three of their own top anthropologists: Baur, Fischer, and Lenz) no more than a mish-mash or compound of many racial strains. But also, the terms 'Aryan', used by the Nazis to describe their 'race', and 'non-Aryan', to describe Jews and others, actually had no racial meaning, having been coined by scientists for the classification of large groups of *languages*. Thus, Aryan takes in not only many European languages, but also the Vedda tongue spoken by Negroes in Ceylon. Likewise, non-Aryan refers to various other languages, including Arabic and Hebrew. But European Jews, who were the principal Nazi victims, were almost entirely Aryan in their language, since the overwhelming majority spoke not Hebrew but Yiddish – compounded of various European languages, mainly with an old German, and therefore Aryan, base – as well as the language of the country in which they lived. The Nazi racial doctrine reached its silliest stage when Nazi scientists obligingly proclaimed their allies, the Japanese, as also Aryans.

On the subject of *race mixing*, the strong feelings have been due to several beliefs. *One*, which we have just shown to be highly questionable, is that a given racial group is superior to another and will deteriorate if genes from an inferior racial group are mixed with it it. *Two*, that if races are kept 'pure' they will each be more outstanding in particular ways (presumably as pure breeds of cattle, horses, or dogs are each better for their particular purposes). But again, we have seen that no human racial groups are pure, or ever have been or could be bred for purity the way domesticated animals have been. If at a given time any human group was or is 'superior' in any respect, one could as easily ascribe this to their having been not pure but mixed, as in the case of Americans, one of the least racially pure and most genetically mixed nationalities the world has seen. *Three* is an old belief that crossbreeding between different human racial strains may result in misshapen offspring. But this also is contradicted by the many fine-looking mulattos in the United States and South America (including some of the most beautiful actresses) and by handsome crossbreeds of many racial strains in Hawaii and elsewhere.

Opposite to the anti-crossbreeding theories is the one that crossing different strains may produce hybrid offspring with greater vigour and other advantages. Livestock and plant breeders have long employed this principle to advantage in combining desirable genes from two different stocks. In early human evolution the same principle might have been effective, but with respect to the present situation we can only make these deductions as to when and how crossing between genetically different groups might be beneficial: (1) If a highly desirable trait (better physique, more efficient internal organs, a special talent, etc.) could be produced by a combination of genes only some of which were carried by one racial group and the rest by another, so that crossbreeding could bring the needed genes together; or, (2) if one group had some hereditary weaknesses and the other group carried 'gene antidotes' for it. However, in the matter of race-crossing (or intermarriage) we are confining ourselves here only to the genetic aspects. The question of whether these matings are socially desirable, when they might lead to family and group conflicts, or personal maladjustment, is outside the field of this book.

With respect to *Negro–white mixing* in the United States, although many assume it has been highest in recent generations, the most race-mixing actually took place in the Colonial days and up to the end of the Civil War. Moreover, where the earlier flow was of white genes into the Negro population, there has since been a considerable backflow of these white genes, plus some Negro genes, into the white population, by way of persons of mixed ancestry who could 'pass'. No accurate figures are available, but estimates (highly uncertain) are that perhaps two million persons of part-Negro descent are now in our white population, and that fifteen thousand or more go over to the white side each year. Since the genes for lighter skin and the less Negroid features are the ones being carried out of the Negro population, this should act to make American

Negroes as a group darker and more Negroid, instead of less so, and to keep them racially distinct from the whites for a long time to come. At present it is estimated that the American Negro population has from 20 to 25 per cent white genes. In addition, it may carry a small percentage of American Indian genes – probably much less than 1 per cent.

Is human evolution continuing? Yes, but not necessarily at the rate it once did, nor in the same way, for a number of reasons: (1) In the earlier stages of man's evolution, more unsettled climatic conditions, higher temperatures, and more intense radiation may have induced more frequent gene changes; (2) human groups have ceased being isolated as they once were for very long periods, which gave greater chance for new hereditary traits to become adapted and fixed in given environments; (3) the process of selecting out for survival the fittest persons, or those with special hereditary traits, has been greatly held down by social changes that permit individuals of all types and kinds (including genetic defectives) to survive and reproduce themselves.

However, new mutations have been constantly occurring in humans, perhaps at the rate of one changed gene in at least every tenth egg or sperm; or, taking sperms and eggs together, at least one in every five fertilized eggs (or children) would be carrying some newly mutated gene. The great majority of these gene changes are very slight, and most are harmful – some extremely so, being newly produced genes for many of the serious hereditary diseases and defects we discussed in earlier chapters. Only here and there do *desirable* mutations occur, which, if the changed genes are passed on and multiply, might lead to hereditary improvements in people. But whatever new human evolutionary changes might have taken place in recent generations, they could hardly have been very great or easy to detect, considering that a century is the merest tick of time in the vast stretches of man's evolutionary history.

In lower animals it has been much easier than in humans to see continuing evolution at work, because they have many more generations in a given period and are less flexible in their capacities to adjust to changed conditions – especially those which are man-made. Thus, within our own time, scores of bird and animal species or types have become extinct or nearly so: including in America alone the passenger pigeon, great auk, heath hen, Louisiana whooping crane, Maine mink, Eastern puma, and various types of bears, elks, and wolves. On the other hand, many *useful* new mutations in various animals have been taken advantage of by breeders, resulting in new types of fox and mink furs, improved types of fowl and cattle, and many new strains of laboratory animals (flies, mice, guinea pigs, etc.). In plants, fruits, flowers, and vegetables, innumerable new mutations in recent decades have also led to the evolution of many important new varieties.

The great fear of scientists today is that human evolution may indeed be speeded up – but in a horrible, reverse way – by the enormous numbers of *harmful* new mutations that almost certainly would be produced if hydrogen or atomic bombs were exploded in any large numbers in a future all-out war. As far back as 1927, before atomic bombs were dreamed of, Professor Hermann J. Muller proved that radiation with ordinary X-rays could increase the natural mutation rate in fruit flies by *150 times*. Later experiments showed that radiation of mice and other mammals – including man – would not only cause gene changes, but would do so to a greater extent (perhaps ten times as much) as in flies. All this has awesome significance with respect to the hydrogen and atomic bombs (and worse still, the possible cobalt bomb), for their powers to produce mutations are infinitely greater than that of ordinary X-ray devices. Not only is it positive that many persons immediately exposed to such bomb blasts would (if they survived) suffer changes in their genes, but the fallout – the rain of radiated particles set loose by the bomb blasts – could spread afar through winds and waters, contaminating plants, fish, and food animals, and causing mutations among people over vast areas. Another danger, even in peacetime, may come from atomic-energy plants. Any careless exposure of personnel to radiation, or careless disposal of irradiated waste products, might easily increase the mutation rate. (It should be kept in mind that under normal conditions mutations are constantly occurring. The threat in atomic radiation is that of adding greatly and dangerously to the mutation rate.)

Genetic mutations can be caused by atomic radiation (as by ordinary X-rays) in two ways: the radiation can act instantly, through direct hits on some genes which cause an upset or rearrangement in the atoms composing them, so as to alter their workings. Or, radiation particles (alpha, gamma, beta, and neutrons) after entering persons' bodies, may find their way into the bone marrow, and from there keep up a slow bombardment of the germ cells to produce later mutations. If the absorbed atomic radiation particles are not by themselves menacing, they can become so when added to the radiation previously absorbed by a person through exposure to X-rays and to natural cosmic rays.

Radiation effects on future children should be distinguished from the immediate effects on unborn babies carried by pregnant mothers exposed to atomic radiation. Studies at Nagasaki and Hiroshima, Japan, after the atomic bomb blasts of 1945, showed that many foetuses were killed or damaged by radiation effects, but not too many malformed babies resulted. However, the *genetic* effects – changes in genes – are not likely to become greatly apparent until several generations have passed. This is because most mutations are slight; or recessive (requiring the coincidence of two of the same genes coming together in a child); or, if producing serious dominant effects, are comparatively rare. Thus, among families of bomb survivors in Japan, reports so far show only slight increases over the average incidence of inherited abnormalities and defects, but geneticists are quite sure that in later generations of these families, especially if persons with the same mutated genes marry, the genetic changes will be more evident. If any of the much more powerful new atomic and hydrogen bombs are dropped anywhere, the genetic effects should become alarmingly obvious.

Will there be 'atomic freaks'? The popular fears in this direction go beyond the probabilities. Actually, any mutations in human genes produced by atomic bombs would hardly be different from those produced under natural conditions, which have led to the many inherited diseases and defects and abnormalities we now have. What large-scale atomic radiation would do, most certainly, would be to increase greatly the proportions of individuals with these conditions in the future.

Could not 'superior' humans result? It is not impossible that among the atomic mutations some might be desirable, leading to improvements in hereditary traits. But as stressed before, mutations are to an overwhelming extent of harmful or defective types – by a ratio of up to 100 to 1 as compared with neutral or desirable ones – and before the superior mutations could take hold they might very likely be engulfed by the bad ones.

Are there men on other planets? Many scientists are beginning to think there may be. But the odds are heavily against these possible others being men exactly like ourselves. It would seem highly unlikely that the very same special evolutionary processes and environmental conditions which produced human beings on this earth could have been duplicated on any other planet, so as to produce similar beings. Even on this earth, should a radical change in conditions wipe out human life (as it once did with dinosaurs), or should man exterminate himself by atomic warfare, scientists doubt greatly whether a species like *Homo sapiens* could again evolve through the chance processes of evolution. One thing seems certain: that mankind now holds its evolutionary future in its own hands. Whether it can turn from destroying its hereditary assets to improving them remains to be seen.

CHAPTER TWENTY-EIGHT

ANCESTORS AND RELATIVES

ONE FREQUENTLY HEARS that a person has this or that kind of 'ancestral blood'. But the term 'blood' is merely a symbol with respect to the relationship of one person to another, since blood itself carries no hereditary factors. No one *inherits* anyone else's blood. As noted in Chapter 2, not even the mother's blood passes on directly to the child she carries, her blood being broken down into its elements before reaching the foetus. From the beginning the developing baby manufactures his own blood, and often his blood may differ even in hereditary type (A, B, O, Rh, etc.) from that of the mother. Thus, sayings such as 'The child carries my blood', or 'Noble blood flows in his veins', or 'He has common blood', are without meaning so far as heredity goes. Equally wrong is the assumption that a person's blood carries any traits of character, as when one speaks of 'impetuous blood', 'tainted blood', 'honest blood', etc. The process of heredity, it must always be kept in mind, is solely and entirely one of passing on and receiving chromosomes and their genes.

Everything any person can inherit from an ancestor must be in the chromosomes received from each parent. No trait of itself can 'skip over' from an ancestor to a descendant. Only chromosomes can be passed along, and these may or may not be the ones carrying the genes which can reproduce the trait of some ancestor. How much of a person's heredity stems from any given ancestor depends entirely on how many of the genes of that ancestor he received at conception. The farther back the ancestor, the fewer of his or her genes a person is likely to have received, to the point where one may have virtually no hereditary link with a remote ancestor, regardless of what the family tree might show.

The only thing about one's heredity of which one can be

certain is that exactly half of one's chromosomes came from each parent – twenty-three from the father, and twenty-three from the mother. Tracing farther back, the number of chromosomes from any given ancestor can only be guessed. For, as explained in Chapter 3, each set of twenty-three chromosomes contributed to a child by a parent may be any one of millions of

Ancestry Theories: Old and New

"BLOOD" THEORY
(wrong)

"A person is a mixture of the blood of all of his ancestors. No matter how far back an ancestor, some of his blood flows in one's veins."

"JIG-SAW" THEORY
(wrong)

"A person's ancestry consists of so many parts of this or that: For example, one eighth Irish, one eighth Scotch, one sixteenth Italian."

"CHROMOSOME" THEORY
(right)

"A person's ancestry consists solely of how many chromosomes of different ancestors he carries. If no chromosome came from an ancestor, there is no hereditary link with him."

different combinations of the chromosomes from that parent's parents. Theoretically the twenty-three chromosomes received from one's father should include eleven or twelve from his father (one's paternal grandfather) and eleven or twelve from his mother (one's paternal grandmother). But actually, any number over half or less than half might have come from either grandparent. For example, among the twenty-three chromosomes received from one's father there might be not eleven or twelve, but fifteen or sixteen of his father's, and only eight or nine of his mother's. Similarly, one might receive proportionately more chromosomes of one's maternal grandfather than of one's maternal grandmother, or vice versa. In extreme cases a person could conceivably have received not more than two or three of a given grandparent's chromosomes, which means that actual hereditary linkage with earlier ancestors on that side of the family might almost be broken off at that point. All we can go by, therefore, are these *average* possibilities of the number of chromosomes of each ancestor one may be carrying:

Grandparents: Average of 1/4, or 11 or 12 chromosomes from each.
Great-grandparents: Average of 1/8, or 5 or 6 chromosomes from each.
Great-great-grandparents: Average of 1/16, or 3 chromosomes from each.
Great-great-great-grandparents: Average of 1/32 – either 2 chromosomes, or only one from each.

Once one goes more than five generations back – beyond a great-great-great-grandparent – the chances become less and less of having a *full* chromosome of a given ancestor. Thus, in the case of a claimed ancestor six generations back (such as, for Americans today, a Revolutionary War hero) the odds would be eight to three against having received a full one of his chromosomes. For an ancestor of the early seventeenth century, such as a Pilgrim, the odds might be twenty to one, or even forty to one, against carrying a full one of his or her chromosomes. We speak of a 'full' chromosome because *parts* of chromosomes might also be passed along. This involves a complex genetic process called *chromosome cross-over*, whereby every so often when sperms or eggs are formed in parents, and two chromosomes of a pair twist around one another, matching sections may be exchanged, or 'cross over', when the chromosomes break apart. Such exchanges of parts of chromosomes over generations increase the chance that a person will have received at least a few of the genes of a distant ancestor. (See also section following.)

When in any lineage there have been marriages between persons with the same ancestor, the chances of a descendant having received chromosomes of that ancestor are increased. For

The "Crossover" Process

How one can inherit part of a chromosome

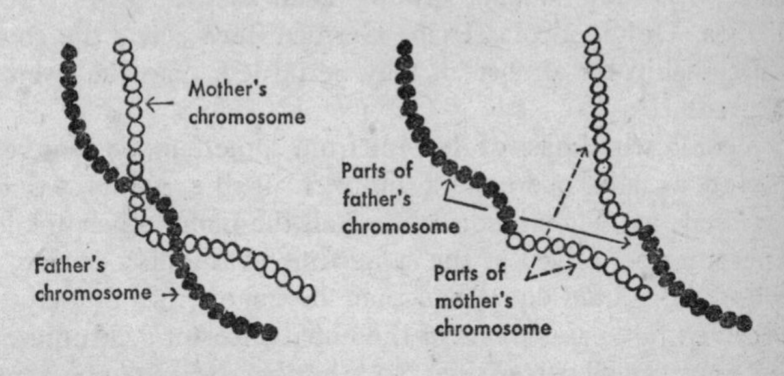

During the egg-forming or sperm-forming process, the paired chromosomes from the two parents may twist around one another.

In breaking loose, matching sections of the two chromosomes may be exchanged, so the new chromosomes formed thereafter have parts from different ancestors.

instance, if one's parents had an ancestor in common, this would double the chance of one's having received some of that ancestor's chromosomes. The more marriages between relatives there were along the lines of descent in a family, the more closely those coming later in the lineage would be linked to earlier ancestors. Thus, present-day members of the much-intermarried European royal families (such as children of Britain's Queen Elizabeth and her husband, Prince Philip, both descendants of Queen Victoria), have much closer ties to remote ancestors than have persons in general. This also applies, in a more limited degree, to descendants of any non-royal close-knit groups among which marriages between near relatives were formerly common. (Colonial Americans, and members of many small communities in Europe, were among these.) Going back far enough into any lineage, of course, there must have been many marriages between relatives, for otherwise the number of anyone's potential ancestors – doubling with each generation back – would eventually reach astronomical and impossible proportions. Thus, it is estimated that all persons of English descent are at least thirtieth cousins; that there is fully as close a relationship within most other European stocks; and that with some smaller groups, such as the Swiss, Swedes, Danes, Dutch, Scots, Irish, German Jews, etc., the cousin-relationship for almost all may be no less than the twentieth degree.

People who boast of descent from some famous remote ancestor usually overlook a number of the points we have stressed: (1) They ignore almost all the many other unknown ancestors who lived at the same time as the famous one, and who contributed equally to their heritage; (2) they may have received not a single one of the noted ancestor's chromosomes (or only a small part of one), and thus have virtually no hereditary link with him; and (3) if they did get some of the ancestor's genes, these may not at all have been those which helped produce his admirable qualities, but may as easily have been his worst ones. Further, traits such as high intelligence, courage, or unusual talent of any kind are so complex that it would be impossible for any combination of genes producing them to be passed along intact from a given ancestor – perhaps not even from a grandparent. The situation might be different for persons who have not one or two, but many distinguished and worthy ancestors, and in whose family line for successive generations up to the present, there were marriages between persons of unusual character and ability. In such cases the descendants might have well above average chances of carrying 'superior' genes.

But rarely do 'superior' marriages or 'superior' offspring continue for too long in any one family line. No human families ever have been or could be bred as were domestic animals –

horses, dogs, cattle, poultry – with thoroughbred strains being produced by mating mothers to sons, father to daughters, or brothers to sisters, and selecting only those with the particular traits desired and discarding the rest. Because human beings have always mated any which way, there is no family that can consider itself as genetically anything but a mongrel mixture, with most of its genes unknown. In any individual case, human superiority or uniqueness rests not in one's claim to distinguished ancestry, but only in what one can prove himself to be in character and achievement.

The many past misconceptions about 'superior' ancestry were accompanied by equal misconceptions about 'inferior' ancestry. In most countries certain family groups were held up (or still are) as horrible examples of inferior heredity. Most often cited in the United States were the Jukes, first brought to public attention in 1874, and the Kallikaks, publicized in 1912. Both families were reported as abounding in mentally defective, insane, alcoholic, degenerate, criminal, immoral, shiftless, and undesirable individuals of every kind – which was blamed almost entirely on their presumed 'inferior' and 'tainted' heredity, in turn attributed to a few degenerate ancestors four or five generations back. Modern science sees the facts in a different light. What appears probable is that the case histories of these families were considerably exaggerated and misinterpreted, since present-day techniques of making such studies were not then available; and that many of the traits blamed on inferior heredity were actually the result of *inferior environment*.

This is not to say that the Jukes and Kallikaks may not have been more than ordinarily defective, or to deny that in some family groups genes for certain types of defects and abnormalities may collect and be passed on in above average proportions, just as in other family groups 'superior' genes may be more prevalent. But, as noted in previous chapters, we are still far from knowing what part, if any, heredity plays in such traits as alcoholism, criminality, 'immorality', or 'degeneracy', and if these traits are concentrated in certain families, we may have to assume – unless proved otherwise – that this is mostly because of the bad environment running in these families.*

One frequently hears a person say, 'I'm one-fourth Irish', or 'I'm one thirty-second American Indian'. In Nazi Germany many people were persecuted or exterminated because they were 'one-eighth Jewish'. And in some parts of the United States the fact that a person is labelled 'one-sixteenth Negro', or less, is sufficient to bar him from white society and privileges. All such references to a person being precisely this or that fraction of a given ethnic group or race have little meaning genetically. The actual hereditary relationship of a person of mixed racial or ethnic descent to any of his ancestral groups depends entirely on the number of chromosomes of that group he carries; and it is impossible to do more than guess about this.

For example, if a mulatto (half Negro) married a 'pure' white person, all their children would be considered, technically, one-fourth Negro. Each child having one and the same Negro grandparent, would, on the average, be assumed to carry eleven or twelve Negro chromosomes. But actually (as explained in a previous section) any given one-fourth Negro child could be carrying any proportion of the Negro grandparent's chromosomes. One child might be carrying many more than twelve, a brother or sister many fewer – to the point of having only one or two Negro chromosomes. Again it would be possible for a person who is technically one-sixteenth Negro to be carrying more Negro chromosomes than one who is technically one-eighth or even one-fourth Negro. Nor can anyone tell from a person's features, or from any known test, how many or how few Negro genes he is carrying. The genes that determine surface appearance are only a very small part of the total genes in a person, and these 'feature' genes may work independently of most other genes. Thus, among offspring of mulattos, a child who looks most Negroid might actually be

* For detailed discussion of the Kallikak study and points involved see the author's article. 'The Kallikaks After Thirty Years,' *Journal of Heredity*, September, 1944; also pp. 525–530 in '*The New* You and Heredity'.

carrying fewer Negro genes than a child who looks most white. All of these facts apply equally to a person who had a grandparent, or other ancestor of any given racial or ethnic group – Chinese, Japanese, Indian or French, Irish, Jewish, etc.

Many of the facts about genetic relationships to ancestors also apply to other kin – brothers and sisters, aunts and uncles, cousins, etc. The hereditary relationship between any relatives, as with ancestors, depends entirely on how many of their chromosomes are the same, which can only be guessed at in terms of averages. The exceptions, other than parents (with each of whom one has twenty-three chromosomes in common), are identical twins, who provide our first example of legal and genetic differences with respect to relatives.

The law makes no distinction between identical twins and fraternal twins, or ordinary brothers or sisters. Yet in the first case there is definite 100 per cent hereditary relationship – all of the forty-six chromosomes in identical twins being the same – while in the other cases there is only an uncertain 50 per cent relationship. That is to say, non-identical children in a family may be carrying any combination of twenty-three chromosomes from each parent; and while on the average half of these may be the same in any two of these children, it is possible that the proportion may be more or less than half. Thus, of several children in a family, two might have not twenty-three, but thirty, thirty-two or more chromosomes in common, and be genetically much closer than either of them is to another child, who might have only eighteen, sixteen, or fewer of the same chromosomes. Moreover, the degree of genetic relationship between any two children of the same parents cannot be proved merely by their similarity in surface traits, because genes in only a few of the chromosomes may be involved in producing these, and it is possible that two children who look less alike may be sharing more of the other chromosomes. In time geneticists believe, or hope, that there will be ways of knowing how many and which chromosomes of given parents the children are carrying.

Certain slight (but sometimes important) differences in the genetic relationship of parents and children, brothers and sisters, result from the way the X and Y sex chromosomes are passed along. For instance, in quantity of genes, a son is at least 5 per cent more related to his mother than to his father. Reason: while of the twenty-three chromosomes a son receives from each parent, twenty-two are the same in the number of genes they carry, the additional X chromosome from his mother has many more genes than the small Y from his father – enough to bring the total genes from the mother to at least 5 per cent over those from the father. (This accounts for the many sex-linked diseases and defects that sons inherit solely through their mothers.) Daughters, since they receive an X chromosome from each parent, have genetically an exactly equal relationship to each.

Uncles, aunts, cousins. The general facts about chromosome relationship given for grandparents and ancestors apply to all other relatives. One can make only an estimate in terms of *averages*, as follows:

UNCLE, AUNT: Each is a one-fourth relative, with the average possibility of carrying replicas of eleven or twelve of one's forty-six chromosomes. The relationship is the same as to a grandparent. (Your uncle, for instance if he is your father's brother, has an average of half his chromosomes in common with your father. And since you have half your father's chromosomes – or half of the uncle's half – one-half by one-half = one-fourth.)

GREAT-UNCLE, GREAT-AUNT, FIRST COUSIN: Each is a one-eighth relative, with the average possibility of carrying replicas of five or six of one's forty-six chromosomes. The relationship is the same as to a great-grandparent. (Further discussions about 'Cousins' in next chapter.)

GREAT-GREAT UNCLE, GREAT-GREAT AUNT: Each is a one-sixteenth relative with the average possibility of carrying replicas of three of one's forty-six chromosomes.

In *disputed parentage cases* blood tests authorized by many courts in the United States and Europe have already made it possible to clear more than half the men wrongly accused of fathering a child. The tests are even more effective in 'interchanged-baby' cases, actual or alleged, when two sets of parents claim the same baby as their own. All of these parentage tests follow the same principle: establishing the baby's inherited blood types in the different systems – A, B, O, Rh, M-N-S, etc. – and then finding out whether the man accused of being the father, or the couple claiming parentage, could have contributed these inherited factors. The tests *cannot prove* that a given man is the father of a given child, or that a particular couple are its parents, because there may be many other persons in the population with the required blood types. But the tests can rule out a man as the possible father, or a couple as the possible parents, if they show that he or they do not have one or another of the blood types needed for the child to be his or theirs.

As one example, if a child's blood is O and a man's blood is AB, the man *cannot* be the child's father, since the child carries neither the A or B factor. If the man does have O blood, a second test might follow, with the MN types: should the baby have the M type, and the man the N type, this would exclude him. If the man does have blood-type M, the tests would go on to the Rh series, and again there might be a chance that the man did not carry the particular Rh gene which would have had to be transmitted by the child's father. Tests of the mother's blood are necessary to give the most complete results. For instance, if a baby's blood is AB, a man with A blood could have been the father. But if the mother's blood is also A, then the father must have been the one who gave the child the B gene, so the A man would be ruled out. Altogether, with the principal blood tests employed today (A, B, O, Rh, and M–N series), a man wrongly accused of parentage has about a 55 per cent chance of being cleared. This, however, is the average chance for a mixed American population, in which divergent proportions of the blood groups and blood types are represented. In a community or group here or abroad where most persons are of closely similar stock, and with small differences in blood types, the chance of parentage exclusion of any man would be greatly reduced. On the other hand, if a man has blood types which are infrequent in a given community or group, his chance of exclusion if wrongly accused of paternity might be very high.

Another use of the blood tests may be in clearing up cases of 'changelings'. Despite the many precautions taken by hospitals today, there are still some rare instances of babies being given to the wrong parents. Since two babies and two sets of parents are involved, blood tests usually can establish whether there has been any interchange. In addition, footprints, handprints, and other traits of parents and children in which heredity plays a part can help to make the proof conclusive.

Occasionally rare inherited physical traits in a child may provide a means of proving or disproving someone's parentage. If a child has an unusual *dominant* surface trait listed in previous chapters (Hapsburg jaw, drooping eyelids, any of various hand abnormalities, etc.) and the mother does not have this trait, its presence or absence in a man accused of paternity might be significant. In some cases, also, certain features or colouring, if their inheritance is clear-cut, might carry weight with respect to parentage. Obviously, if a baby has black hair, dusky skin, and jet-black eyes, and the mother is a fair-skinned, blue-eyed blonde, a man who is also fair, light-haired, and blue-eyed is hardly likely to be the child's father.

However, one must be extremely cautious about forming judgements or suspicions regarding parentage on the basis of a few surface traits. Many hereditary traits do not show themselves or become set until late in childhood, or in the mature years, and thus have no value if decisions must be made regarding an infant's parentage. Further, the mere resemblance or lack of resemblance between a person and a given infant need not offer proof or disproof of parentage, since a child may sometimes be quite unlike either of its true parents in colouring and other feature details. But taken altogether, a number of inherited feature traits could have a bearing on parentage cases where the blood tests are inconclusive.

CHAPTER TWENTY-NINE

PARENTHOOD PROBLEMS

INTERESTING AS THE subject of human genetics may be, its main importance lies in the practical contributions it can make to human welfare and happiness. True, the application of genetic principles has led to vast improvements in plant and animal breeding, with better quality and increased production of grains, fruits, vegetables, beef, poultry, milk, and virtually every other major cultivated food product on today's tables. In antibiotics, applied genetics has greatly increased the production of penicillin, streptomycin, and other disease-fighting organisms. But in these and many other ways, the achievements of genetics have come through working with *non-human* genes. What has been, or can be accomplished, by applying the principles of genetics directly to the improvement of human genes and human breeding? In this and the next chapter we will present some of the answers.

At various points in this book it has been shown how the knowledge of human genetics has swept away many superstitions, false beliefs, fears, and harmful theories about heredity that have plagued people for ages; how it has helped to give parents and children a better insight into their biological relationships; how it has clarified the nature and causes of many diseases and defects and made possible better medical diagnoses and treatment; how such specific findings as those relating to the Rh factor have aided in saving the lives of thousands of babies; how with respect to traits of intelligence, achievement, talent, and behaviour, we are now better able to identify the relative roles of heredity and environment, and deal more fairly and sensibly with individuals; and how the facts regarding race and ancestry are all working to promote better understanding among human beings in general. Now we will take up some of the ways in which human genetic findings can guide persons in important individual situations.

The most common of the personal heredity problems involve fear of inheritance or transmission of defects, diseases, or other undesirable traits. In each case, once it is clear that a given condition *is* hereditary, decisions must be governed by its severity; the nature of its inheritance and the risk of transmission; the stage of life at which it appears; the degree of its interference with happiness, work, or adjustment; and how prepared parents might be to have and rear a child so afflicted. Further, whether or not there is immediate danger of a defective child, socially minded persons might be concerned about passing on the defective gene to future generations. (See next chapter.) With respect to many of these points, the general answers can be found in preceding parts of this book. Where more specific guidance is needed, it may be obtained from various qualified persons, depending on the nature of the problem: if chiefly *medical*, from physicians specializing in the disease or defect; if chiefly *genetic*, from medical geneticists (see Appendix); if chiefly ethical, moral, or social, from one's spiritual adviser or a qualified marriage counsellor. Here are some of the situations for which advice is often sought:

1. *A couple have had one seriously defective child.* Should they risk having another? One must first be sure about the nature of the condition. Many congenital abnormalities are purely environmental, due to prenatal accidents or the mother's temporary condition, and may not occur again. (The doctor in the case can best determine this.) If the condition is clearly hereditary, the chance of a repeat with another child may be great or small, depending on the method of inheritance, as shown in the accompanying table of repeat threats. In any case one should not make the common error of thinking that 'lightning doesn't strike twice', or that if the risk of having a defective child is one in four, for example, once one has appeared the next three will be normal. As with a dice number turning up, two or three genetically defective children may appear in succession. On the other hand, the risk of a repeat is often so small that a genetic

adviser may tell the parents not to hesitate too much about having more children.

CHANCES OF A 'REPEAT' DEFECTIVE CHILD

(Whether hereditary or not)

If a couple has had one child with this defect:	*The chances of having another child with the same defect are:*
Idiocy	
Mongolian	1 in 50
Amaurotic or phenylpyruvic	1 in 4
Cretinism	Uncertain
Hydrocephaly	1 in 60
Feeble-mindedness (IQ 50 to 70)	
If both parents normal	1 in 10
If one parent a moron	Up to 1 in 5
If both parents morons	Up to 3 in 4
Schizophrenia	Up to 1 in 12
Albinism	1 in 4
Clubfoot	Up to 1 in 30
Harelip (with or without cleft palate)	Up to 1 in 7
Spina bifida	Up to 1 in 25
Extra fingers and/or toes	Up to 1 in 2
Malformed hands or feet (hereditary types only, listed in Chapter 13)	Up to 1 in 2
Hip, congenital dislocation	1 in 30
Heart, malformed	1 in 50
Kidney, polycystic congenital	1 in 4
Intestines, pyloric stenosis	1 in 17
Any other hereditary defect or abnormality mentioned previously in this book:	
If recessive	1 in 4
If dominant	1 in 2

(Risks for either of the above are much reduced where the condition is listed as 'qualified'.)

2. *A couple who have not yet had children are hesitating about having any*, because one mate is afflicted with an extremely serious hereditary condition.

– If the condition is a clear *dominant*, it will probably be transmitted to *one in two* children. With the risk so great most genetic advisers might counsel against having children. For 'dominant-qualified' conditions the risks are smaller, but still ominous.

– If the condition is *recessive*, there will be no defective child unless the other mate is carrying a gene for exactly the same defect. Clues as to whether this is so may come from that mate's family history, and in the case of some diseases, from tests. (See Chapter 11, 'Forecasting Disease Inheritance'.)

– If the condition is *sex-linked* (usually with the gene in the X chromosome), and if the husband is afflicted, there will be no children with the defect, but there is a fifty-fifty threat for each of his daughter's sons. In some of the very serious sex-linked conditions (haemophilia, certain muscular atrophies, certain blindness conditions, etc.) there would be every reason for afflicted men not to have children.

3. *Both members of a couple have serious hereditary defects.* If these are *dominant*, the facts in 2 (second paragraph) apply even more strongly. If the defects are *recessive*, the important point is whether they are exactly the same ones in both mates. If they are, *all* the children might be affected. But if the husband's and wife's hereditary afflictions are entirely different, *none* of the children might have either defect. However, every child would become a carrier of two defective genes.

4. *Neither member of a couple* (*married or contemplating marriage*) *is defective*, but serious hereditary defects have appeared in close relatives of each. Here again, the question is whether the defects on both sides are the same or not, and how they are inherited. If the defects are the same, and *recessive*, there is a chance both mates are carrying genes for it, and might produce a defective child (but with the risk no more than one in four). If the recessive defects are different (as, for instance, some form of hereditary blindness on one side, deafness on the other), no

child would be likely to have *either* defect, since matching genes would be required from both parents. If the conditions running in both families are clearly *dominant*, the fact that both mates are free of the conditions would prove they are not carrying the defective genes, so there would be no threat to their children. However, in *dominant-qualified* conditions, or those with late onset, there cannot be the same certainty. (See Guide, end of Chapter 11.)

5. *A couple with all the children they expect, and none yet defective, are nevertheless concerned for the future because of hereditary defects in close relatives.* Is there reason for such concern, and does it help any to worry? Sometimes, yes, if the hereditary defects or diseases are among those whose appearance depends on environmental factors, or on age, or both. For instance, if childhood rheumatism, diabetes, cancer, mental diseases, allergies, etc., have appeared in families, there should be alertness to possible symptoms in the children, and special precautions should be taken if needed. Especially hopeful is the fact that as medical science has been tracking down the causes of various hereditary defects and diseases, and linking some of them with abnormalities or upsets in the body chemistry, the chances of reducing their seriousness through early detection and treatment is increasing.

6. *A young man and woman, much in love, are hesitating about marriage because of certain bad traits in relatives of one or the other* – criminality, drunkenness, sexual abnormality, etc. – which they fear might crop up in their children. As we saw in previous chapters, there is little evidence that such behaviour traits are hereditary, and even if they were, their transmission would be so complex that a child would run virtually no chance of 'inheriting' these tendencies of a grandfather, uncle, or aunt. Nothing in the situation as stated should prevent a marriage; in fact, if the man and woman are themselves normal, of good character and well-adjusted, any genetic risks would be outweighed by the advantages they bring to a marriage.

Popular fears that cousin, or near-relative, marriages may result in seriously defective offspring have a basis in fact, although the threats are often not as great as many imagine. The risk in these marriages can be simply explained: when a husband and wife are closely related, they have a much greater than average chance of carrying the same genes; and if any of these genes are bad ones – particularly serious hidden recessives – there is a much above average chance that a child will receive a double dose of the same harmful gene, and be defective. For example, *first cousins* are alike in *one eighth* of their genes, on the average. Should one of them, even though completely normal, be carrying a gene for any recessive defect (idiocy, albinism, hereditary blindness or deafness, etc.) the other cousin would have a one-in-eight chance of carrying a matching gene; and if this were actually the case, there would be a one-in-four chance of having a child with the defect. But if one cousin is himself (or herself) afflicted with a recessive defect – which means carrying two of the genes for it – the chance of the same gene being present in a first-cousin mate is *one in four*, and if it is present there is a fifty-fifty threat of their having a defective child.

In any harmful hereditary conditions requiring certain genes from both parents, the genetic risks for offspring of first-cousin marriages are much above average. Moreover, while the rarity of a condition decreases the probability that two unrelated parents will both be carrying the gene for it, in the case of first cousins, once one carries a given gene, the chance that the other also carries it is always the same, regardless of the condition. In marriages of *second cousins*, with one in thirty-two genes in common, and third cousins, with one in 128 genes in common, the risk of their having defective children is naturally much smaller than with first cousins, but is still far above the average for non-related persons.

As evidence of the foregoing, in groups where there has been much inbreeding, the incidence of certain hereditary defects is often unusually high. This has been found true in some isolated rural communities in the United States (Martha's Vineyard, Chesapeake Bay peninsulas, Kentucky mountains) and in some sections of Switzerland, Sweden, Japan, and other countries, where the cousin-marriage rate has reached close to 10 per cent. In these groups there are much above average incidences of one hereditary defect or another, including feeblemindedness, deafness, albinism, and dwarfism. Equally true, in many other groups, the rarer a recessive defect, the more one is apt to find that afflicted persons are offspring of marriages between relatives. In *albinos*, close to one in five have parents who were first cousins, and in some rarer conditions the ratio may reach even higher. In amaurotic idiocy about one in six or seven cases stem from first-cousin marriages, and many other cases would show marriages between relatives farther back. However, in all groups and most countries the proportion of defectives with cousin parents has been decreasing as the incidence of cousin marriages has steadily declined. Reasons: increasing movements of people, which are breaking up close-knit groups; greater opportunity for young people to go afield for their mates; and decrease in family sizes, which has cut down the number of cousins available for marriage. In the United States and most modern countries first-cousin marriages are now much under one per cent (except in some rural areas), and eventually may occur not oftener than one in three hundred times, or less. (Laws against first-cousin marriages in twenty-eight states of the United States may also have been a factor in decreasing their incidence.)

Where there is a reasonable assurance that no serious hereditary defect has appeared in their mutual family line for some generations, the genetic risk in marriages between cousins may be relatively small. Thus, there is little evidence that extensive inbreeding among the Puritans, the ancient Spartans, or more recently, the Pitcairn Islanders – the highly inbred descendants of the famed mutineers of the *Bounty* – had any especially harmful effects. In families of unusually sound stock and superior qualities, cousin marriages may even tend to produce superior children. That is to say, where there are concentrations of certain 'superior' genes (as for high intelligence, musical talent, artistry, or good qualities of various kinds), marriages between cousins will increase the chances that desired gene-combinations will be passed on to offspring. In some families, therefore, the possible good results might offset the risks.

One might note that Charles Darwin was married to his first cousin, Emma Wedgwood (of the famed china makers), and

Cousin Marriages

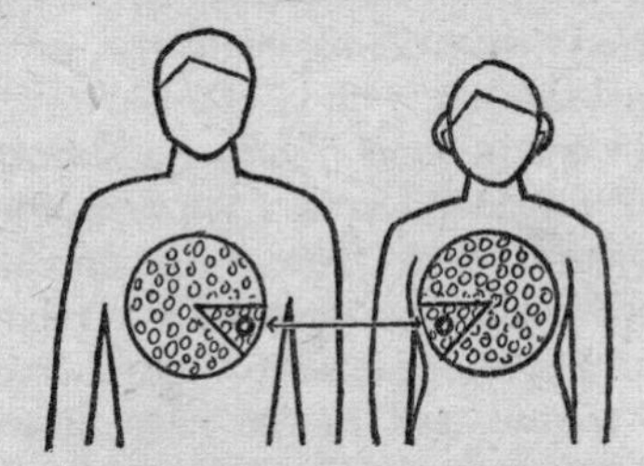

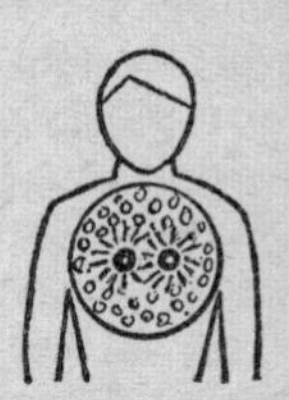

One eighth of the genes of first cousins are the same. If one cousin carries a hidden (recessive) bad gene, the chance is one in eight the other has the same gene.

If first cousins marry, the risk is thus much above average that a child will receive two of the same bad genes, and will develop the recessive defect.

had many distinguished descendants. Abraham Lincoln was also the product of a cousin marriage. In the Bible one finds many examples of close-relative marriages with notable descendants: Jacob, married to his first cousins, Rachel and Leah; Abraham married to his half sister; and Amram married to his aunt, and siring Moses, Aaron, and the prophetess Miriam. In the royal families of ancient Egypt marriages between brothers and sisters were the rule for generations (Cleopatra having descended from six generations of such marriages), and apparently were not harmful to offspring. All of this, incidentally, would show that there is no 'natural instinct' against incest among human beings (any more than in lower animals) but that such prohibitions against near-relative marriages which are found in taboos, laws, or religious proscriptions, usually arose from social, psychological, or assumed genetic reasons.

Finally, fears of hereditary risks may apply not only to people's own children, but to children whom they might want to adopt. In former times the fears regarding hereditary traits in children of unknown or uncertain parentage who were offered for adoption tended to be grossly exaggerated. Today, many of these old fears have been greatly lessened as the demand for babies to adopt, in the United States particularly, is vastly exceeding the supply. If there is a genetic risk in an adopted baby, it is recognized that every child of one's own is also a genetic gamble to some extent. One offsetting advantage in the case of babies offered for adoption is that prospective foster parents can at least make sure that there are no obvious defects to begin with. Reputable adoption agencies also report any risks that the baby may present, and permit its return if any serious inborn defect shows itself in the near future. (Usually there is a probationary period of six months or more for both child and foster parents.) With respect to the ultimate 'character' of an adopted child, there is a tendency now to believe that it will be determined much less by the behaviour traits of the true parents than by those of the foster parents, and by the environment and training they provide.

CHAPTER THIRTY

EUGENICS

WHEN GOVERNMENTS AND religions avow that 'All men are created equal', it is recognized that this refers to the rights of all human beings under the laws of God and man to be given fair and equal treatment. No one can be unaware that Nature does not follow this principle in fashioning people's minds and bodies, but brings individuals into the world with many inequalities in their inherent make-up and chances for survival, achievement, and happiness. This fact has been a troubling one throughout history, and has given rise to various notions, practices, and plans. In some groups, such as the Spartans, defective offspring were killed (as they still are among various primitive peoples). Other groups have assumed that they could grade themselves into 'superior' and 'inferior' hereditary classes born and bred for different roles and stations in life. Still others have felt that their own racial or ethnic group was inherently destined to dominate – and if they wished, to exterminate – 'inferior' peoples (the latest example having been the Nazis). Beyond this the thought has always persisted that, inasmuch as human beings could successfully breed lower animals for improved and special qualities, why could they not control their own breeding towards more desirable goals? Some of the many problems raised by this question will be dealt with now.

The term *eugenics*, derived from the Greek *eugenes* ('well-born'), refers to measures for improving the hereditary make-up of the human species. Eugenics is not a science, and should not be confused with genetics (as it often is), although as advocated today it draws on genetic principles. However, when the eugenics movement was launched and named by Sir Francis Galton, in England in 1883, the science of genetics had not yet come into being. Thus, at the beginning, the eugenics programme was based on many wrong beliefs regarding the inheritance of various traits, the division of people into inborn 'superior' and 'inferior' stocks or classes, and the manner in which 'unfit' individuals could be quickly bred out of the human species and a race of 'supermen' produced. Because of the extreme attitudes and proposals of many early 'eugenists', and their failure to distinguish between the effects of bad heredity and bad environment, their movement met with much opposition. In recent years this has changed considerably, as the eugenics proposals have become sounder, more conservative, and better adapted to new scientific facts and social changes. Thus present-day eugenics advocates have come to include many respected geneticists, social scientists, and population experts.

What has concerned many authorities has been a lopsided trend in the childbearing situation: on the average, parents who are most 'fit' – those most educated (and perhaps also most intelligent), successful, healthy, socially advanced, and able to do most for their families – tend to have proportionately the fewest offspring. At the other extreme, parents considered less 'fit' – the least educated (and often least intelligent), least successful, living in unfavourable environments and able to do least for their families – tend to have the most children. This is a reversal of the situation in former times, when the most 'fit' and successful families, living as they did under the best conditions, had the most children. The chief reason for the change, of course, is that in the groups which today are most advanced, childbearing is voluntarily limited to a much greater extent than in the less advanced groups.

The important eugenic question is whether the parents producing the most children today, on the average, are genetically inferior, particularly in mental ability, to those producing fewer children. If so, mankind's hereditary qualities would be deteriorating. But there is no clear evidence on this point – only deductions from a few facts. As noted in Chapter 19, IQ's of children tend to follow the levels of their fathers' positions, being highest for children of professional men and executives, and grading down to lowest for children of unskilled workers.

But here there is question of how far IQ's (except among defectives) actually measure or reflect differences in inherited basic intelligence. Many would maintain that IQ tests are so much slanted towards educational factors that the lower IQ's of the socially backward large-family groups are due to their inferior opportunities. Others maintain that making full allowances for environmental effects, the genetically superior persons would have been more likely to have risen to the top in any group, and that the high IQ's of the more advanced and successful individuals, and of their children, do on the average reflect higher levels in inherited intelligence. On this basis, since the higher IQ groups have been producing fewer children and the lower IQ groups proportionately more, it has been claimed that the general level of basic intelligence in countries such as England and the United States has dropped several points in the past few generations. This assumption cannot be considered proved.

Whatever the facts might previously have been, recent social, educational, and economic advances have made the birth-rate picture less extreme. There has been a considerable increase in childbearing in the more 'fit' and educated groups, particularly in the United States; women college graduates, of whom a very large percentage used to remain spinsters, are now marrying and having children almost up to the general average; and more and more professional women are combining careers with motherhood. At the same time an increasing proportion of parents from the former backward ranks have been upgraded into the 'fit' ranks; there has been a decrease in the birth rates of groups formerly considered less 'fit' or advanced, as the birth-control practice has spread; and the placing of proportionately more mental defectives in institutions has withdrawn them from the ranks of possible parents. (Sterilization of defectives will be discussed later.) Nevertheless, there continues to be enough difference in the undesirable aspects of the birth-rate and genetic picture to make many authorities feel that certain measures should be taken. These are of two types, 'positive eugenics', to increase the numbers of 'fit' individuals, and 'negative eugenics', to decrease the numbers of the 'unfit', in all groups.

Negative eugenics involves all measures that, theoretically, could prevent or reduce the births of 'unfit' individuals – those so defective that they would be a burden to their families, a detriment to the world and would themselves find no happiness in being born. The measures proposed would leave the prevention of such births almost entirely to voluntary action by the potential parents (except in the case of those mentally unable to decide for themselves). Not only hereditary, but environmental threats would be considered. Whatever the cause, couples who are low-grade morons, or insane, or criminal, or degenerate, are not likely to be 'fit' parents, and limiting their reproduction might be good for society. However, some of the eugenic steps proposed to combat this are highly controversial. Particularly, there has been certain religious opposition. In discussing some of the suggested negative eugenic measures we are not necessarily recommending them.

The preceding chapter presented various genetic situations in which persons might feel justified in not having children, or not having more than those already born. Opposition to preventing or limiting reproduction in these cases, it should be clear, *is not to the principle* involved, but to the means. For instance, Roman Catholic authorities have stated that where there are strong probabilities that a genetically defective child will be produced, avoidance of conception may be justified; and where parents have as many children as they can hope to educate, rear healthily, and provide for suitably, or as the mother can bear without overtaxing her strength, limitation of reproduction is sanctioned. (Statement by Pope Pius XII in November, 1951.) The Catholic opposition is to control of conception by *artificial* – mechanical or chemical – *means*. What is permitted is only 'natural' control, either by abstinence from sexual relations or confining them to the so-called 'safe period' in the woman's menstrual cycle. The latter, or 'rhythm' method, however, while able to reduce considerably the chances of conception, is often unreliable and ineffective, since a woman's fertile period cannot always be established with certainty. It might be noted that there is no formal religious opposition to birth-control methods among the great majority of Protestants and Jews (except for a few sects in each), nor among most Hindus, Buddhists, or Mohammedans. In a number of Asiatic countries (India, Japan) government programmes of birth control are already under way, primarily to keep the population from growing out of bounds.

The most extreme method of birth control is an operation that permanently prevents reproduction. In a woman the Fallopian tubes, which deliver eggs to the womb, are cut and tied; in a man the tubes that carry sperms from the testes are likewise cut and tied. (Neither operation has any effect on a person's desire or capacity for sexual performance.) Such operations are legally authorized in twenty-seven American states (although not carried out in all), and in some European countries (mainly Scandinavian), in cases of individuals who are mentally defective or insane and are likely to produce mentally defective offspring. Sterilizations also are authorized in a limited number of other cases, involving serious hereditary defects, and in some states (chiefly California and Indiana) for habitual criminals, habitual sexual offenders, and 'degenerates'. (The latter sterilizations are chiefly for social reasons, since there is no proof that such persons are products of defective heredity.) Altogether, from 1907, when the first American sterilization law became effective (in Indiana) until January 1955, 57,218 legal eugenic sterilizations were performed in the United States, 34,282 on women, 22,936 on men. Of these, about half were for mental deficiency, 44 per cent for insanity, the rest for other causes. In addition, it is estimated there have been from one thousand to two thousand private sterilization operations annually in the United States, some on individuals who feared they might transmit serious hereditary defects, and some on women whose lives would have been threatened by childbearing (as in certain cases of nephritis, heart disease, etc.).

What can sterilization accomplish? Initial hopes that many

of the worst hereditary defects could be quickly and easily wiped out by sterilizing the afflicted persons have been much deflated by these findings:

1. The most common of the serious hereditary defects are *recessive* or otherwise due to multiple genes, which means that persons who are themselves afflicted are only a small proportion of those carrying the genes. For instance, for every hundred thousand hereditary morons, there might be a million persons carrying single 'moron' genes. Thus, sterilizing all those with recessive or multiple-gene defects would not prevent most of the genes involved from being passed on, so the proportion of defectives in future generations would be only slightly reduced.

2. In *sex-linked* defects we again have the problem of the carriers. Most of these conditions afflict only or chiefly males (Chapter 11). But sterilizing these defective males would still leave the biggest proportion of the genes to be transmitted by female carriers. While one can tell when a woman is such a carrier if her father has or had the sex-linked condition, or if she has had an afflicted son, sterilization might be justified only in extreme and rare cases. (Haemophilia, or some sex-linked muscular, eye, and mental defects.)

3. *Dominant* hereditary defects, caused directly by a single gene, could be greatly reduced in incidence by sterilizing those affected. But the serious dominant conditions are rare. Moreover, new gene mutations usually keep replenishing these defects, so they might never be completely wiped out. Also difficult to eradicate would be the qualified or partly dominant genes, whose effects may 'skip' the parent but crop out in a child, and genes for conditions with late onset which may not appear in a parent until after the children are born.

But there are many objections to any broad-scale sterilization programme. One reason for the present 'go slow' attitude towards sterilization is the fear that it might get out of hand. This was shockingly shown during the Nazi terror reign, when vast numbers of men and women were sterilized on the flimsiest eugenic grounds, or merely because they were of political, racial, ethnic, or religious groups of whom the Nazis disapproved. Other reasons are the growing possibility that treatments will be found to reduce the threats of many hereditary defects (as has happened with diabetes); the fact that some persons who are genetically defective in one way (blindness, deafness, muscular afflictions, etc.) may be genetically superior in other ways; and, not least, religious opposition. However, should means be found to produce sterilization temporarily, or only for as long as desired, many of the objections to it might be lessened or eliminated. The 'contraceptive pill', recently developed, may offer such a means.

Positive eugenics refers to any measures which could lead to the improvement of the human stock by increasing the proportion of healthy, intelligent, capable, and useful persons. Some of the recommended steps, as noted before, already are being carried out through economic and social advances in the United States and other countries. Earlier marriages and earlier childbearing, when mothers are healthiest, are producing more children and healthier children in the 'fit' groups. Better prenatal and child care, and vastly improved medical treatments, are reducing the proportions of defectives in all groups. Increased income for young persons, subsidies from parents, hospitalization plans, unemployment benefits, social security, etc., are easing worries about having and rearing children among those who want them most and can do most for them. All these steps were once basic planks in the positive eugenics platform.

As part of the programme of helping 'fit' persons to become parents, great progress has been made in overcoming many cases of sterility and bringing children to previously barren couples. In up to one in three sterility cases the cause may lie in the husband's failure to produce fertile sperms, or sufficient sperms, which need not be related to disease, health, and/or virility. Where the wife has been barren it may be because of her inability to produce fertile eggs, or if she does conceive, to carry a child through to birth. In close to a third of the sterility cases the difficulties can be overcome.

Artificial insemination is a controversial process that has been employed in recent years in some cases where the wife is fertile but the husband is sterile, and the sperms of another man are used to conceive a baby. (In occasional instances the method is resorted to if there would be hereditary risks in the husband's fathering the child.) One might note first that artificial insemination is now widespread in livestock breeding, perhaps 15 per cent of all dairy cows in the United States, and many race-horses, being bred by this method. In the case of humans the procedure began to be used several decades ago, and since then perhaps forty thousand babies have been conceived in the United States in this way.

In all artificial insemination cases the first requirement is that the husband must consent and will accept the resulting child as his own. With this provision, a qualified medical expert then obtains fertile sperms from another man and injects them into the wife. From a purely physical standpoint the method has proved effective and satisfactory. The donors whose sperms are used are carefully selected, being mostly young college men of good health, character, and hereditary background. In each case the donor, or proxy father (whose identity is kept secret by the doctor), is 'matched' as nearly as possible with the husband's colouring, appearance, racial stock, and blood groups. The wife is then inseminated at her most fertile time, and when she is in the best state for motherhood.

It is estimated that at least one million couples in the United States are childless because of the husband's sterility, and could have children if they utilized the artificial-insemination method. The fact that only an extremely small proportion do (from two to three thousand annually), can be ascribed to these reasons: (1) *Psychological* – most often the husband's antagonism to the procedure. However, once the initial objections are overcome, only a small fraction of the artificial-insemination cases have led to any marital conflict. (2) *Religious* – artificial insemination with other than a husband's sperm was condemned as 'illicit and immoral' by Pope Pius XII in 1949, and was also opposed by the British Archbishop of Canterbury in the same year. However, many Protestant authorities have approved the method when it helps to bring children to otherwise childless couples. No formal opposition has come from Jewish sources. (3) *Legal problems* – many complex legal aspects of artificial insemination (when the sperm used is not the husband's) remain to be settled. In the very few instances that courts have so far dealt with the problems raised, conflicting opinions have been given. A New York judge ruled in 1948 that a baby born of artificial insemination is not illegitimate. A Chicago judge ruled to the contrary in 1954. At the time of writing the question has still not been legally resolved in the United States.

Looking ahead, there is the possibility that, by the quick-freezing process, human sperms may be stored for long periods, and that human 'semen banks' may become available for inseminations. In the breeding of lower animals, including prize livestock and race-horses, the practicality of the semen-freezing and storing process has already been demonstrated. Extended to human beings, it was reported at the University of Iowa in 1954 that four recently born babies had been conceived through inseminations with previously frozen and stored sperms. If such storage can be continued successfully for years, it may bring to reality the theory that in some future time the sperms of a great man may be used to sire hundreds of children long after his death.

In line with the preceding statement, there is also the fantastic possibility that some women in the near future may be able to have children *without bearing them*: by transplanting the fertilized egg from one woman to the womb of another, who will then mother the foetus through to birth. Experimentally, this transplanting of eggs (and sometimes whole ovaries) has already been carried out in lower animals (cows, dogs, rabbits, and mice). In all of these cases, it is important to note, the offspring, in their hereditary traits, were *as much like the mother from whose egg they developed as they would have been had they grown in her own womb*, and in no way developed traits of the proxy mother. Back of these lower-animal experiments is the thought that eventually any prize or thoroughbred female – horse, cow, dog, etc. – will be enabled to produce many more offspring than she could alone in the normal way, by having various other females mother her eggs. With respect to human beings the process of employing proxy methods may have great value some day for women who can produce fertile eggs and conceive, but are unable to carry children through to birth because of uterine deficiencies, or for whom motherhood would be dangerous because of certain diseases (nephritis, heart ailments, etc.).

Growing out of some of the remarkable breeding techniques now successfully used with lower animals may be the thought that they could also be used to produce more and better *human* thoroughbreds. The idea is appealing. *But* – who is to decide what types of human beings we should breed for? Lower animals are bred for only a few specific traits; one is not concerned with the other traits. A horse may be a speedy racer, but no good for heavy work. Or a dog may have a fine-shaped head and body, but be quite unintelligent. A desirable and successful human being, however, must have a great many unique qualities, each of them highly complex and dependent on a great many genes. We have seen how difficult it would be merely to breed out serious defects – even those produced by a few simple genes. There would be far more difficulty in trying to *breed in* almost any of the 'desirable' traits – superior minds, great talents, fine characters – the complex genes for which have not even been discovered. Most difficult of all would be trying to combine in one stock of humans not merely these traits, but also beauty, strong physique, and superb health. Finally, when we consider that thoroughbred cattle, horses, and dogs are the products of hundreds of generations of selective breeding – and that a generation for these lower animals is a fraction of a human generation – any extensive plan to breed 'superior' human beings must seem remote, if not also dangerous.

In this atomic age, the power of human beings to destroy themselves or warp their genes is clearly much greater and more imminent than their power to improve themselves and their genes. There is little question, then, that the immediate hope for human happiness lies primarily in making the most of what genes we already have, and of the power they carry to change and improve our environment. This power that lies in the human gene is vastly greater than that which lies in the atom. We can explode the atom and cause destruction. We can develop and utilize the power within the gene to do untold constructive good. As we learn to understand our genes, we will also learn to better understand ourselves and our fellow men, and how to manage our lives for the greatest benefit to all. In the end, human beings can never be more than their genes permit them to be. They should strive not to be less.

SUGGESTIONS FOR FURTHER READING

For more detailed information regarding most aspects of human heredity, the reader might turn first to the author's comprehensive work, *The New You and Heredity* published by Chatto & Windus Ltd. This is one of the few popular treatises. The other books in the following list are mainly technical works and are recommended for students and professional readers.

REFERENCE BOOKS AND TEXTBOOKS

Harris, H. *Human Biochemical Genetics.* Cambridge: Cambridge University Press, 1958.

Roberts, J. A. Fraser. *An Introduction to Medical Genetics.* Oxford University Press, 1959.

Fuller, John L., and Thompson, W. Robert. *Behavior Genetics.* New York: Wiley, 1960.

Garn, Stanley M. *Human Races.* Springfield, Ill.: Thomas, 1961.

Hsia, D. Y. *Inborn Errors of Metabolism.* Chicago: Year Book Publishers, 1959.

Kallmann, Franz J. *Heredity in Health and Mental Disorder.* New York: Norton, 1953.

Stern, Curt. *Principles of Human Genetics.* 2nd ed. San Francisco: W. H. Freeman, 1960.

Wallace, B., and Dobzhansky, T. *Radiation, Genes and Man.* New York: Holt, 1959.

PERIODICALS DEALING WITH HUMAN HEREDITY

Except for the two eugenics publications, which are popularly written, the following journals are technical and recommended mainly to students and professional readers.

Acta Geneticae et Gemellologiae. (Published in Rome, Italy, and giving special attention to twins.)

American Journal of Human Genetics. (U.S.A.)
Annals of Human Genetics. (England)
Eugenics Quarterly. (U.S.A.)
Eugenics Review. (England)
Human Biology. (U.S.A.)
Journal of Heredity. (U.S.A.)

WHERE TO GET ADVICE

HUMAN HEREDITY CLINICS

Authoritative information and advice on problems of human heredity may be obtained at the following institutions. In most cases, however, if the person applying is a layman, it is advisable that contact be made first through one's physician, particularly if the problem is a medical one.

The Genetic Clinic, Institute of Child Health, Hospital for Sick Children, Great Ormond Street, London, W.C.1.

Leeds Department of Child Health, University of Leeds Medical School, Leeds, Yorkshire.

Department of Child Health, Medical School, The University of Bristol.

The Heredity Clinic, Medical School, The University of Liverpool.

INDEX